MAN'S PLACE IN THE DYBOSPHERE

By Richard R. Landers

Prentice-Hall, Inc., Englewood Cliffs, New Jersey

To Barbara and Gary—May they find happiness in the Dybosphere.

Second printing .... March, 1967

Man's Place in the Dybosphere by Richard R. Landers

Library of Congress Catalog Card Number: 66-26132 / Printed in the United States of America / T 55206 / Prentice-Hall International, Inc., London / Prentice-Hall of Australia, Pty. Ltd., Sydney / Prentice-Hall of Canada, Ltd., Toronto / Prentice-Hall of India Private Ltd., New Delhi / Prentice-Hall of Japan, Inc., Tokyo

Preface

There exists a simple experiment that was quite in vogue half a century ago but is now so rarely demonstrated in classrooms that the majority of the readers of this book may not even have heard about it.

The equipment required is simple indeed, consisting of a pane of glass (measuring, say, 4 by 6 inches), a sliver of glass not more than ¼ inch in length and quite thin that has been coated with shellac, and a large drop of chloroform. A large magnifying glass is useful, but not essential. The drop of chloroform is placed on the glass pane to avoid spattering, then the shellac-coated glass sliver is pushed across the glass pane until it just touches the chloroform.

Instantly there is activity and it looks as if life had been suddenly created. The drop of chloroform transforms itself into something that acts like an amoeba. It engulfs the glass sliver, greedily "eating" the shellac. When all the shellac has been absorbed, the glass sliver is ejected by the chloroform drop and everything is serene again.

This little experiment is based on rather simple chemical reactions but was as astonishing (and a little frightening) to lay audiences prior to the first World War, as are automated machines, space capsules, super-fast computers and other such devices today. In reality, with the proper background, one is as understandable as the other.

There is of course a difference. You don't have to "feed" shellac to a drop of chloroform; but you cannot escape the new environment of automatic devices and computers, all doing things that seemed to have been reserved for very skilled hands and exceptionally bright brains.

One can say that all this is just the "second stage of adaptation." During the first stage Man adapted himself to the environment he found; the second stage is adapting the environment to Man's needs. The machines we have created and continue to create are becoming part of the environment. Many people wonder where this will lead. Of course there is no final answer; but this book tells what is going on and what is likely to happen.

Willy Ley

CONTENTS

PART I
EXPEDITION
TO THE DYBOSPHERE

Chapter One

Introduction

Since I am intimately involved in today's pervasive and, at times, overpowering technology, perhaps I can contribute to an increased understanding and acceptance of our machine-dominated world— a new world, not that we discovered but that we made. It is a world of mechanized men and humanized machines.

One can hardly read a magazine, a newspaper or even a comic strip without realizing that machines are an intimate part of our intellectual, artistic, moral and social lives. And these technological developments have a profound effect on our thinking and behavior. Even the *subject* of technology provokes an intensely emotional response. Many damn automation with words as depersonalizing, dehumanizing and even demasculinizing. Others bless it in equally unrealistic terms.

Objectively, technology can provide greater security, comfort, health and dignity. Any change of great magnitude alters life patterns, modifying and reshuffling social, political and economic thought. But technological change has the unique property of containing within itself the means for solving the problems it creates. If the tension and strain of modern living can cause ulcers, the advances in medical technique enable a cure—and perhaps ultimately a prevention.

Technological advances are moving us from the biosphere to the dybosphere. We are all familiar with the former; the realm of the

3

living. We study the structure and function of animals and vege-
tables, the relationship of organisms to each other and the environment. But we are not consciously familiar with the *dybosphere;*
the realm of artificially created things which behave in a life-like
manner. Perhaps we are too confused and frightened.

How did this world develop—by revolution or evolution? Do we
want to live in the dybosphere—and are we free to choose? What
will happen to our society, government, jobs when machines become even more dominant than they are today? In short, what is
the dybosphere and man's place in it?

To illustrate some features of the dybosphere let us examine a
typical modern home. Hardly anything in it is "natural." The artificial flowers look natural but they are actually made of plastic. The
fruit on the simulated wood-grained plastic table looks real but is
made of wax. The house itself is "manufactured" from either
synthetic materials such as concrete blocks, or processed natural
materials such as plywood. Note the adjectives "artificial," "simulated," "manufactured," "synthetic," "processed"—and how they
imply "deceptive," "cheap," or "inferior."

The dybosphere can also be characterized by the many devices
which increase the efficiency of some purposeful human action such
as lifting, or ones which replace a human function such as calculating. To understand these labor-saving and mind-supplementing
devices we might see how they developed vis-à-vis the drama of
human endeavor. First to appear were tools, then machine tools,
and finally machines.

Act One finds early man using existing natural objects to increase
his efficiency but not to replace any human function. The earliest
tools were sticks for digging food from the ground, gourds for carrying and storing liquids, rocks for breaking open nuts, and the like.
Gradually the fittest saw that if they walked more erectly, developed
greater manual dexterity and, most important, thought a little
harder, they could use the tools more advantageously. Thus while
man developed the tools, to a considerable extent the tools developed man!

When primitive man made a useful object, he built it according
to a purposeful design, invariably patterned after the artisan's own
bodily designs but more specialized, and thus more effective. A bowl
would simulate cupped hands; a club with a stone head was simply

an improved arm and fist; a flint scraper was a larger and stronger fingernail. (It was natural, too, for man to think that the gods also built according to a design and made everything to fit a purpose. And even later on, man believed that a battering ram could not be effective unless the head of the device was actually shaped into the head of a ram.)

Toward the end of the First Act, we see the man of antiquity modifying his natural tools somewhat for even greater efficiency. Bone and wood handles are tied onto rocks so that greater force may be applied when hammering; bone splinters have eyes drilled into them so that they can be used as needles for sewing; notches are made in flintstones for use in sawing.

At the beginning of the Second Act, we see man using outside sources of power to supplement his own energy. Windmills, water-wheels, and oxen treadmills begin to power machine tools. The tools, such as grinding stones for milling grain, are part of a complex of machine parts which includes gears, levers, pulleys, inclined planes and so forth. During the middle of the Second Act, the semi-automatic machine tool appears. This makes products and requires no human intervention other than setting up the work piece, starting and stopping the machine and removing the finished part.

And toward the end of the Second Act, the machine tool has developed to the point where the human is no longer even an operator but a monitor, for this type of machine tool is generally controlled by a punched or magnetic tape which contains all of the directions required for fabricating a product. This high point marks a reversal of roles in the man/machine tool relationship. Before, the human operator was in direct and continuous control of technological devices. Now the machine tool itself assumes the operative functions. Yet, man is still dominant and does provide the intelligence necessary for making slight adjustments.

At the start of the Third Act, man no longer plays the leading role, and the machine tool has been replaced by a device called, simply, a machine. It is a rather crude one that clinks, hums and buzzes. But, while it is mainly prompted by man, it does provide a limited amount of intelligence. It solves simple production problems and is adept at the repetitive and speedy calculations required for operational control.

Toward the end of Act Three, we note a vast improvement in

the machine's capacity and performance. Not only can it see, hear and feel but it is also capable of self-improvement.

This Act has not yet ended but the script is clear—the machine will become a first rate performer—logical, creative, imaginative and original. Some say the Machine (notice the capital M) will try to steal the show. There are those who say "he" (you really can't say "it") may even bring down the house. So if the play did drag a little in the First Act, and was merely impressive during the Second, the finale will be smashing. There is no doubt that machines as a group will dominate man as a group and, eventually, individual machines will dominate individual men.

By dominate I mean control, regulate, restrain, influence, pervade, direct, guide, prescribe, etc., by virtue of superiority in all aspects of tasks demanding a leader.

Consider the "captain of a ship." In the days of iron men and wooden ships, the captain was the supreme authority (that is, completely dominant). With the advent of steam ships and of radio communication the captain of a ship was still in charge but machines navigated and steered. Currently, in the case of airplanes, the pilot is the captain; but with automatic equipment it is—or soon will be—a fifty-fifty proposition as to who actually runs the ship. The equal sharing of responsibility between man and machine is the crossover point; presently there are equal tasks for man and machine. Ten years from now (or relatively soon thereafter), the airplane pilot will be titular captain of the craft and everything from takeoff to landing will be performed by the "automatic" pilot. The same process is taking place on ships where crew members are being replaced, one by one, by automatic controls and the captain is becoming, more and more, a "passenger."

After the crossover point there is obviously a reversal of dominant roles, or an inversion. This term, in a technical sense, denotes the "turnaround" maneuver that a radar or human observer must make as an airplane passes overhead as it is watched or "tracked" from horizon to horizon. The inversion maneuver in both humans and radar represents a highly unstable situation. Tracking continues until the target passes slightly beyond the directly overhead position (that is, until the neck or antenna reaches its mechanical limit of travel). Then there is confusion and hesitancy in determining which way to turn around. Fast moving targets are often lost in this null zone or blind cone, as it is called, because the inversional response is too slow. The reversal of man/machine dominant roles, in the same way, requires a well-timed inversional response.

The historical progress of man can be compared to a descending airplane; the historical progress of machines to a second airplane, going in the same direction but ascending. Both man and machines are at transitional points. Mankind is at the age individual man reaches when he has more years behind him than in front of him— about 42. Machines, conversely, are about 14—too old to be called children and yet not old enough to be called adults. Needless to say, both transitional (or inversional) ages are awkward and confusing.

We are witnessing a point in time which, for convenience, is called the crossover point, and marks the end of a man-dominated world (biosphere) and the beginning of a machine-dominated world (dybosphere).

Jacques Ellul, in *The Technological Society,** uses the term *inversion* in a similar way. In discussing technique or technology in the broadest sense, he says: "Herein lies the inversion we are witnessing. Without exception in the course of history, *technique belonged to a civilization* and was merely a single element among a host of nontechnical activities. Today *technique has taken over the whole of civilization.* Certainly technique is no longer the simple machine substitute for human labor. It has come to be the 'intervention into the very substance not only of the inorganic but also of the organic.' "

Machines are becoming more sophisticated, reliable, faster, and their environments are becoming more extreme. Consider the pilots of two supersonic passenger airplanes headed on a collision course. They are approaching each other at a closure rate of 5,000 miles per hour. Assuming they see each other at a distance of fifteen miles, they will have one second to react, manually reach for, and grasp a control. Radar extends the pilot's "vision" to around 90 miles; but in this case too it is simpler to feed a collision signal into the autopilot—which reacts in thousandths of a second—than to flash a warning light or ring a bell for the pilot.

There are machines which fly higher and faster than birds; which

* Alfred A. Knopf, New York, 1964, p. 128.

travel as deep and faster than fish; which see farther and in less light than eagles; which read and calculate faster than man. If machines have changed so radically in twenty to forty years, what will they be able to do in the future? Man's growing concern is to keep from being overtaken—figuratively and literally. To quote Emerson, "Things are in the saddle and ride mankind."

If this is so, and in a sense it is, then surely we must "turn around" and look at machines anew.

Chapter Two

Dybology

A *very great part of the mischiefs*
that vex this world arises from
words.

—*Burke*

At one time, in the not too distant past, things were either living or they were not. This is essentially true today. However, there are an increasing number of things that even though they are not alive, in our accepted meaning of the word, they behave remarkably like living things. This behavior consists of such humanlike characteristics as remembering, learning, goal-seeking, decision-making, irritability, adapting to environment, and ability to reason. That we have machines which can walk, talk, speak, see, and generally behave in a rational manner is common knowledge. There are even machines in the process of development which are capable of growth, self-repair, self-reproduction, and self-sustenance. Whether such machines are capable of feelings and emotions becomes not so much an academic question as a problem in semantics. For if a machine requires these characteristics to perform its duties, there are valid reasons to believe these "emotion functions" can be built into them.

Yet, how can we clearly and directly talk about things that are vaguely alluded to between quotation marks? When we say a computer is a "giant brain" we are not being precise. We are either hedging through ignorance or willfully sensationalizing for effect. Our newspapers and technical literature are full of such quote-clouded words and phrases (although it must be admitted that the quotation marks tend to fade away with repeated usage). For example, computers are now invariably referred to as electronic brains

9

without anyone feeling the need for qualifying quotation marks. But then another form of limiting coloration takes place by the use of adjectives such as artificial, simulated, ersatz, and synthetic.

The practice of endowing mechanical contrivances with terminology related to the human body is an old one. Starting in Middle Ages and in current use today, for instance, various pipe organ parts are referred to as the "foot," "toe," "mouth," upper and lower "lips," and "teeth." Some pipes have projections called "ears" and "beards." In the 15th and 16th centuries, pipes were decorated with faces. Because the original organs of the time were one-man creations, the master builder looked at each instrument of his artistry as having a personality of its own: a "soul" breathed into it with the tone of its pipes.

In medieval times, personifying man-made articles was not semantically inconvenient; it was in keeping with the romantic nature of the period. But today this practice does not seem as appropriate, at least in a strictly technical sense. (The air filter of an automobile is not called a nose nor is the combustion chamber called a stomach.)

The situation can be compared to that of a boy named John Jones, Jr. Calling him Junior when he is young is acceptable to all. However, this becomes awkward as he reaches maturity. Although technically correct and proper, continuing to add junior to the name seems to attenuate rather than increase John's identity.

The same is true with machines and machine elements. Now that the products of our technology have reached a form of maturity, it is appropriate to refer to these complex and life-like products more in terms of the products themselves than in terms of their origin or biological likenesses.

Of course, this is similar to the mice deciding to tie a bell on the cat in the sense that it is easier suggested than done. To treat machines in their own right requires a framework on which a pattern of ideas, notions, concepts, sentiments, and observations can be formed. An independent framework such as this depends essentially on some central theme or thought. But how does one express a thought when there is no existing word for the key element of the thought? Just as snowflakes need a speck of solid material around which water vapor can crystallize, so do new concepts need a vocable whereby vague ideas can crystallize.

As I wrote more and more articles and books about machines, I became aware of the feeling one gets when he remembers various scenes of a movie but can't tie the plot together because the name of the movie escapes him. For example, I wrote about the personality traits of machines, maturation curves of machines, clinical diagnosis of machines, and the behavioral changes that take place in a machine as it moves through the various phases of its life cycle. The realization that machines resembled humans in many ways grew stronger (of course the thought was hardly original; there have been many who have said this centuries ago), but exactly how and why the resemblance existed eluded me.

My thinking was indistinct and I could trace this fuzziness of expression only to an insufficiency of words. I was fully aware of Voltaire's admonition that when people talk about a thing they do not know, they use words they do not understand. However, my problem was not the misuse but the lack of words. Because of this, I was forced to use analogies and comparisons that often strayed from—or at least distracted from—the subject. An engineer does not mind using analogies to clarify a point, but (as the Talmud long ago admonished) one cannot prove a point with an example.

After a considerable period of searching for the key term which would unlock the vague concepts that were forming in my mind, I finally did pinpoint the word I had been looking for, but quite by accident.

When writing, I often put a dash in a sentence for a word that does not come to mind quickly in order to retain the major thought. The particular sentence I hurriedly wrote was "A ———— consistent norm of behavior for electronic equipment is a failure rate of two parts per thousand per month." The thought in the sentence was important to the article as it represented its key point. Omitting the word that was represented by the dash and saying "A consistent norm of behavior for . . . . etc." was insufficient. Without the modifying adjective represented by the dash, the result would be a tail-chasing tautology (something like saying the average was the most usual). The question could rightfully be raised, "Consistent with what?" (Or, "What average are you talking about that is the most usual?") The elusive word was cornered, but what was it? I then made use of a mathematician's device which suggests: If you do not know how to solve a problem, try solving one just like it. Unable to find the word represented by the dash in my original sentence, I tried an equivalent sentence in a different field of effort. The sentence that came to mind was, "A biological consistent norm of behavior is a body temperature of 98.6°." It became immediately clear that I was looking for a word that was equivalent to *biological*, but which applied to complex electromechanical equipment. With this realization it quickly dawned on me that the word I had been looking for did not exist! There was no word like biology to designate the thought of life-like *but artificially created* things. There was no recourse but to develop a term to fit the need.

Having decided to coin a new word, I realized that the task should not be undertaken lightly, for in selecting the term I would be naming a science essentially the equivalent of biology. There was no question in my mind that this new science already existed —as did biology long before it was so named in 1813—and that work was already going on in such areas as artificial intelligence (computers), artificial eyes (television), artificial voices (radio), and artificial ears (sonar).

About 1958 when the above semantic exploration took place, I was also searching for a new approach in order to make equipment more reliable. The practice then, as it is now, consisted of making each part of the equipment as long-lasting as possible. For some reason this did not seem to be a practical solution because electronic equipment was growing in complexity to the point where single subsystems already contained hundreds of thousands of parts. The failure of almost any of these parts would cause a failure of the entire system.

In casting about for a new approach, I hit on the obvious (in retrospect) idea of copying nature. The human body, for example, has billions of "parts," most of which last only days or weeks, yet the body as a whole has a life span of about 70 years. This concept of duplicating cellular growth and replacement led me to believe that if this process were carried to its extreme, the ultimate machine would be a man!

After further thought, I realized that instead of going too far in this concept, I had not gone far enough. While I was mentally humanizing machines, the realization struck me that the process of mechanizing humans was also taking place (through the use of eyeglasses, hearing aids, artificial arms and legs, electronic-heart pacers and so forth). This latter considered trend, if carried to its ultimate extreme, indicated that the ultimate man would be a machine!

How to reconcile these two parallel trends: humanization of machines and mechanization of men? At some future point—certainly a theoretical one—the two trends would meet. In other words, the machineman and the manmachine (there is no reason to hyphenate these words) of the future would probably be identical. I then approached my colleagues with this "unified concept." One quickly pointed out that there would be a difference; the manmachine would have a soul, the machineman would not. This triggered off a number of thoughts of my own. I vaguely remembered when researching the term biology that an archaic meaning of the Greek word bios, from which biology was derived (i. e. *bios*, life and *logos*, description) was *soul*. Here was a starting point, at last, for finding the desired word. All that was required was a word for an *artificial* soul (that is, one not assigned by human effort as in the case of the medieval pipe organs). Fortunately, there is one that is quite close. In Hebrew mythology there is the term *dybbuk* (dib-buk) which means "unassigned soul." Taking the first three letters *dyb* and adding the vowel *o* for sonance, produced the prefix *dybo*. From this, it was easy to arrive at dybology, the "artificial" equivalent of biology.

Of course, the similarity of *dybological* to *diabolical* was quickly noted by my colleagues.* (The similarity was exaggerated by the tendency to mispronounce the *y* in the prefix *dyb* as a long *i*, as in die, rather than the correct short *i*, as in rib.) In any event, I had to admit that the similarity between the two words could be prophetic as well as phonetic.

Having set a goal to find or to coin a word meaning life-like but artificially created, and then having synthesized this neologism, I was faced with a problem: What to do with a new word? I didn't use it in the sentence, "A dybological consistent norm of behavior for electronic equipment is. . . ." etc. Even though it was the correct word, few others would know what it meant. I explained

---

* In addition, medieval superstition considered dybbuk to be a migrant soul and sometimes an evil spirit which leaves the body of a man and then invariably possesses the body of some innocent person. The spirit or dybbuk could be removed only through religious exorcism.

the dybological concept in several discussions (man and machines were becoming more and more alike), but in magazine articles, technical papers, and books, the newly coined word was used in a context where its meaning would be obvious. In fact, in the patent application for a self-growing, self-repairing, and self-sustaining machine, I used the term *dybloc* in reference to the replaceable elements in the machine (similar to biological cells) without mentioning that dybloc is the contracted form of dybological block and without explaining what dybology itself is.

The reason for underselling the word was deliberate. I had noticed the negative reactions to any one who is presumptuous enough to coin a new word. For instance, an outspoken executive of a large electronics company bluntly told me that he would have thought the dybological concept was wonderful if I had not given it my own title. I realized that new ideas took a long time to germinate. Also, a new word is difficult to force into the language. Need generates acceptance, not advertising.

Obviously, a new word does not automatically represent a new idea but it often generates a new concept. Usually an idea that has been around for a long time has grown so ripe that it just begs to be named. Having a new word—or words—provides a fresh tool with which archaic notions can be removed and new ideas created and molded into shape. Putting a name on something that is awesome in its semiformed state is like pulling up an attic shade; shadowy objects can then be seen in a brighter and less frightening light. The point is that we tend to fear things we do not understand. Almost without exception, scholars, and others feel compelled to warn us to "turn back before it is too late." And what are we being warned against? Such things as the destructive machines which allegedly dehumanize art and culture; which supposedly suppress the richness and idiosyncrasy of personal existence; and which seem to transform natural foods into standardized, uniformly colored and packaged, highly advertised, trade-named technical products. Of course, there are some valid features in these warnings, but in the bright light of reality and understanding we see that it is not a tiger stirring about in the attic but only the house cat. An analysis of current-day trends reveals great changes are taking place which should be welcomed for the opportunities they offer: the opportunity to distill out the valuable and useful from the harmful and burdensome.

Further, I had been presumptuous in the past to claim originality for any idea. I discovered many people develop "original" concepts on their own, but when they carefully research the subject, they invariably find that someone had the same idea a hundred years ago —if not a thousand—and expressed it most clearly.

Let me cite an example. People have felt the need to speak out in recent years on the "threat of machines." They strongly feel it is their duty to warn the rest of us that machines may take over the world. But I have yet to read any statement that puts the idea more eloquently than Samuel Butler's in his book *Erewhon*, written in 1872. After first pointing out that even in 1872 more men were tending machinery than their fellow man, he asked the question "Are we not ourselves creating our successors into supremacy of the earth? Daily adding to the beauty and delicacy of their organization, daily giving them greater skills in supplying more and more of the self-regulating, self-acting power which will be better than any intellect?"

Dybology identifies a growing area between biology and engineering that cannot be classified as being strictly biological, or strictly engineering. (These will be discussed in greater detail in the following chapters.) There are biologists employed in manufacturing firms who are searching for new mechanical devices based on biological principles. For example, investigation is being conducted on an improved sonar device patterned after a bat's ability to navigate by emitting and listening to high frequency squeals. Also, there are engineers working in medical research laboratories to help produce electromechanical organs to serve as replacements for diseased or damaged human organs. While courses already are being conducted in the combined area of biology and engineering, as biomedical engineering, they are conducted in either medical or engineering colleges. It is reasonable to assume that the future importance and magnitude of these courses will grow to an extent that they will require a new type of college; one that is independent of the two founder disciplines. In this way we can expect schools of biology, engineering, *and* dybology. I also feel that the person implanting (installing) and treating (servicing) mechanical hearts (pumps) in the future, while perhaps working under the direction of a physician (chief mechanic) will certainly have to be a specialist in this area of work—a dybologist.

What will the dybologist study? In addition to the more conventional courses already being taught, he will study such things as dybophysics, dybochemistry, dybometry, and dybodynamics. While there is little need to further explain these terms (as long as it is understood that the prefix *dybo* means life-like, but artificially created), it can be seen that dybophysics is the branch of physics dealing with life-like matter; dybometry deals with the measurement of the probable failure-free duration (reliability) of life-like mechanisms; and dybodynamics deals with the functional processes of life-like mechanisms.

Notice the phrase, "life-like, but artificially created," is used to define dybology, rather than the more probable, "life-like, but man-made." The choice of *artificial* over *man-made* is to avoid any awkwardness that might arise. Certainly for some time in the future, all dybological things will be made by man. But restricting the term to only the handiwork of humans is like clipping the tail feathers of a bird before it has learned to fly. Currently machines are being considered that will be self-reproducing. And while these machines may need the constant care and attention of humans for a considerable period, there is reason to believe that the equipment of the future will be completely self-generating and self-supporting. In any event, just to discuss the theoretical possibility of such an eventuality requires the new term, dybology.

Speaking of theories, we can refer to *biogenesis*—the theory that living organisms come only from other living organisms and not from non-living matter. This theory, while a big step forward from the previous, but now rejected, theory of *abiogenesis* (which stated that life is spontaneously generated, as in flies from spoiled meat) currently is accepted almost as a universal truth. Yet, the theory of biogenesis can be shattered any day when artificially created—but indistinguishable from the real—life is created in one of the many laboratories working toward this objective. We will then require a parallel theory of *dybogenesis*, which will state that not all life comes from previously existing life.

Not to belabor the subject of life-origins, we should at least acknowledge and examine the awkwardness which arises because the finished fabric of a substance is often confused with the loom upon which it was woven.

A number of laboratories in the United States and Europe are investigating the origins of life in the early days of the solar system. By duplicating the conditions believed to have existed four billion years ago in the primitive atmosphere of our earth, these "test-tube life" studies try to join simple chemical compounds into more complicated ones. This primeval atmosphere is thought to have consisted mainly of hydrogen, methane, ammonia, and water vapor. The theory is that by subjecting this atmosphere to the bombardment of the sun's radiation, cosmic rays, and lightning, chemical compounds are formed which are the physical basis of life. Sugars and amino acids have already been synthesized in this manner. Current work consists of the formation of viruses from ribonucleic acids and proteins from amino acids. These infectious virus particles are laboratory produced chemicals which reproduce themselves and, in a sense, grow. One by one, the barriers separating living and non-living are being broken.

If these experiments prove successful in creating single-celled living things such as protozoa and bacteria, then the *life* created will not be "artificial" but "natural." The experiments will have duplicated a process which took place long before any higher form of multicelled organism existed, including man. That is, the newly created life will be as natural as any other in existence but only its *method of generation* will be artificial (i.e., nature simulated).

The above discussion has the kernel of an important point; one that will save endless confusion and permit us to accept the dybosphere for what it is without a great deal of frustrating inner conflict. The emotional reactions being referred to are those some people have when eating with a person who has artificial arms. They perhaps would feel less disturbed if the person were fed by someone else. The absence of organic arms is an unfortunate tragedy, but having cosmetic (non-functional arms) somehow seems more "natural" than the mechanical appendages.

Consider the situation from the unfortunate person's point of view. To him, the mechanical arms are not only natural, but they are real—they *are* his arms. He would possibly agree that the *origin* of these arms is artificial, but to him it is the only thing that is. The fact that these arms are made of metal, plastic, and the like is only a matter of academic interest. To him, it is a difference in degree, not in kind.

The above discussion does not imply that a mechanical arm is identical with a biological arm (although the original inference that original life and artificially created life would be identical is still maintained). However for all intents and purposes a mechanical arm is real and natural to a person who uses one.

And at some risk, I will go further. There will be a time in the not too distant future when mechanical substitutes—assuming they are required—will be preferred over a biological transplant. To illustrate, it is likely that heart transplanting and mechanical hearts will both be perfected reasonably soon. Patients, consequently, will have a choice between biological and dybological hearts. The heart produced by nature is a stable and time-proved standard model. The man-made heart, while undoubtedly not too reliable in early models, will be improved continuously in performance, endurance, size, weight and so forth. There is little reason to believe that the mechanical heart will not be more efficient and effective than the one we were born with; and when this is so, a dybological heart no doubt will be chosen over a biological heart.

To sum up the discussion thus far, we have seen that language is one of the many problems technology presents; we have traced the generation of the prefix *dybo*—meaning life-like, but artificially created—to help solve the semantic problem; we have made the observation that new words more often reflect new concepts than create them; and we have seen that confusion could be held to a minimum if words were taken only for what they are—labels for ideas—rather than the idea itself. All this is to indicate that language, the predominant factor in social and technical organization, is both a reflection and a causative agent of current thought; changes in the pattern of language represent changes in people and vice versa.

While reviewing, let us examine more closely the meaning and uses of *dybology*, since the term represents the central theme of this book.

Dybology as a word denotes the field of study that deals with everything inanimate, but life-like. It can be used to denote those segments of art, engineering, and science which are concerned with artificial creations. It can be used in a philosophical sense to help describe the super-mechanical environment (dybosphere) we are creating for ourselves.

There is a current trend to exchange technical and scientific language in traditionally distant areas of knowledge. For example, we find "umbilical cords" on missiles and "negative feedback" in humans. As the similarities between living organisms and machines become greater than the differences, the choice is to either create new words at the risk of bewilderment or use the same words and invite confusion. The more efficient practice in the long run is to use the same words and merely identify the frame of reference in which they are being used.

Biology is already available to identify the animate point of view or frame of reference and, desirably, dybology identifies the inanimate, but animate-like, point of view or frame of reference. For example, in describing a computer that performs the function of a human brain, we need not go through the awkwardness of putting "brain" in quotation marks, as has often been the practice, nor do we have to refer to it (quite erroneously) as a mechanical brain, but simply state that it is a dybological brain.

A true story in this regard may be illustrative. To help in the work being done on self-repairing and self-growing machines, we hired a medical student for summer work. (His friends, who spent the summer conventionally interning in hospitals, jokingly called him an MD—a Missile Doctor.) One day in connection with a rocket launching, he overheard the comment, "We had an abortion due to a twisted umbilical cord." Quite surprised he asked, "Are you speaking biologically?" "No," I answered, "Dybologically."

Anyone who has done serious writing about behavioral aspects or maintenance actions associated with machines soon realizes the limitation of available descriptive terms. The vast majority of words to describe functional states of activity (e.g., tired, sleeping, sick) or corrective actions (e.g., operate, dissect, amputate) essentially apply to animate things. Most of the words currently used to describe functional states of machines, or maintenance actions performed on them, are either slang or semi-technical at best. For example, a "sick" engine is "on the fritz" or the radio that stops functioning "pooped out" or perhaps "went on the kibash." The semi-technical terms (but the only ones available) used to describe symptoms of television malfunction observable on the picture tube screen are: rollover, hash, jitters, motorboating, gear-toothing, and herringbones.

Surprisingly, there is no word for machines which is comparable to the word healthy, as applied to humans. Until one is coined, or perhaps until the word healthy itself is adopted in a dybological sense, we will have to be content with phrases as "tip-top shape," "really humming," "hitting on all cylinders," or simply "perking." And as previously mentioned, just as "human" words and phrases are applied to machines such as "the engine died," mechanical terms are applied to people. For example, "He is ready for the junk heap," "I am rusty," or "Don't blow a gasket."

Leaving the area of slang and semi-technical words let us examine the scientific use of dybological words. In the scientific sense we do not simply "make up words" but rather employ the established principles of "etymology." Unfortunately, the results in most cases are more disastrous than they would be if we simply accepted slang. For example, instead of "trouble shooting" we would have "etiology." Or, in the case of removing a relay we would have a relayectomy (in the same sense removing tonsils is a tonsillectomy). We would ultimately arrive at stickyvalvitis, motorbrush hypotrophy, a hyperthermiatic engine, and pneumonoultramicroscopicsilicovolcanoconiosis (silicosis, the medical term for a miner's lung disease)!

The question becomes whether or not Greek or Latin prefixes, middles, and suffixes should be used in technical and scientific areas of machine development and repair. In the field of medicine, this is widely accepted. The physician's scientific language was developed essentially in times more staid than the present: a time when Greek and Latin were the universal language of the learned. Today, however, engineers when dealing with mechanical subjects tend to use more colloquialisms than literary forms.

The intention here is to highlight rather than to solve the semantic problems associated with our exploding technology. If offering one family of words relieves this problem, *dybology* will probably serve the purpose.

As we have examined the specific meaning of dybology, we must also examine the meaning behind the meaning. Each neologism has a reason for being coined and dybology is no exception. If anything, the circumstances surrounding this new term had accumulated into a state which was overripe for naming. While Samuel Butler, in his satire, *Erewhon*, did not name the "state," he came close in referring to it as the "mechanical kingdom." * Dybology, therefore, is to the mechanical kingdom as biology is to the animal and plant kingdoms.

But naming something in seriousness is quite different from a satiric reference (although I do not doubt for a minute that Butler was extremely serious). Does this mechanical kingdom lend itself to a taxonomy whereby machines are classified into subkingdoms, phyla, orders, classes, species and the like? Let us consider the possibility. Although there has been no modern-day Linnaeus to perform the task, it can be seen that the dybological kingdom divides easily into mechanical systems (transportation, water distribution, etc.), electromechanical systems (production, warfare, etc.), and electrical systems (power distribution, communication, etc.). The systems in turn can then be categorized into subsystems (railway, fractional distillation, and power stations), and the subsystems can be split into major equipments (locomotives, condensers, and turbogenerators). This classification can be continued down to the nut, bolt, relay, and transistor level.

I can imagine two archeologists of the distant future digging in the buried ruins of a factory. One will pick up an object and ask his companion, "And what species of nut do we have here?" "Why," his companion answers, "I do believe it is a National Coarse, 14 threads per inch, castellated hex head—long extinct, but hardly rare."

If machines can be classified in some hierarchical order, do they lend themselves to genealogical examination? Here we are on firm ground, for tracing the historical descent for various equipment is a common practice. The Automobile Museum at Cleveland's Historical Association has a chart giving the lineage for each family of automobile, by manufacturer. This large chart with hundreds of entries traces the various generations of automobile descendants

---

* "Is it not plain that the machines are gaining ground upon us when we reflect upon the increasing number of those who are bound down to them as slaves, and of those who devote their whole souls to the advancement of the mechanical kingdom."

from the granddaddy of them all, the Winton. Of course, the gene-
alogy of transportation devices can be traced farther back to the
carriage, the wagon, the cart, and the Indian travois poles.

How about evolutionary development? Although most people
who had not previously thought about the subject would disagree;
even a casual examination shows that machines are subject to and
obey essentially all of the evolutionary laws set forth by Darwin.

Natural selection takes place on the product designer's drafting
board countless times a day. Value engineers—a new breed of specialist—make a fetish of fitting hardware to the function required
of it while reducing its cost. Selection of the right component for
the right job in modern machine design is more than natural selection; it is accelerated selection. While nature is satisfied to allow
a thousand generations to pass in order to pick the best from the
better, these value engineers (or value analysts, as they are sometimes called) feel one extra generation is too long. The survival of
the fittest machine—particularly in a free economy such as ours—
occurs in every showroom, store and market place.

Mechanical mutations appear in startling form and with amazing
frequency: transistors, where there used to be vacuum tubes; jet
engines, in place of reciprocating engines, ball point pens, instead
of fountain pens, and so on.

Creations of cross-fertilization are common. To cite three examples: in hybrid computers (analog and digital), hybrid rocket
engines (solid and liquid fuels) and hybrid microelectronics (monolithic semiconductor and thin film). The growth, tenure, and
extinction of various species of machine is a daily occurrence; lasers
found commercial application several years after their discovery
and the first computer, at the ripe old age of only fifteen years, has
already been museumed with the reverence shown a dodo bird.

Evolution, in its broadest sense, is apparent in all of our machines. Taking just one type of machine, the intercontinental bal-
listic missile, we can start with a rock (the payload) and an arm
(the driving force). Continued and unbroken development can be
traced from the stone-tipped spear, the arrow and bow, the bullet
and gun, the shell and cannon, the bomb and bomber plane, and
the current warhead and rocket engine of guided missiles.

But some will say that the above reasons for adding machines to the Darwinian evolution is based simply on analogy: they say that the parallels drawn between machines and biological organisms are at best perhaps only slightly more than coincidence or a play on words; there is little to support the machine's application for membership to that elite group from which only the fittest survive. These guardians of natural selection demand more credentials.

Primarily, they want to know if a machine can produce offspring of its own kind; if there is provision for variability (as opposed to producing 100 per cent carbon copies); and if some machines have a greater chance of survival than others. The answer to all these questions is, yes. A machine can be self-reproducing, can provide for variability, and can even of itself select unplanned but fortuitous changes.

The nature of the evolutionary development (whether strictly Darwinian or not) of machines is hardly as startling as is the speed with which such development is occurring. The previously mentioned Samuel Butler, in the last century, pointed out the extraordinary advance made by machines during the last few hundred years when compared to the relatively slow advances of the animal and vegetable kingdom. He noted that the more highly organized machines were creatures not so much of yesterday but of the last five minutes. Butler shows keen insight when he says "Do not let me be misunderstood as living in fear of any actual existing machine; there is probably no known machine which is more than a prototype of future mechanical life. The present machines are to the future as the early Saurians to man... what I fear is the extraordinary rapidity with which they are becoming something very different to what they are at present. No class of beings have in any time past made so rapid a movement forward. Should not that movement be jealously watched and checked while we can still check it?"

To those people who seem to think that man will be able to keep up with the machine's development he states, "We cannot calculate on any corresponding advance in man's intellectual or physical powers which shall be a set-off against the far greater development which seems in store for the machines. Some people may say that man's moral influence may suffice to rule it; but I cannot think it will ever be safe to repose much trust in the moral sense of any machine."

However, while complex machines do make mistakes and can be destructive, I have no fear of avarice, deceit, cupidity, fraud, guile, and all the rest from machines.* Unfortunately (or in this context fortunately) these are strictly human traits. I am certain that machines will remain morally pure.

* Except to the extent that they are recapitulations of the human beings who created them. That is, the destructive purpose of a machine cannot be hidden easily (Orwellian slogans to the contrary) since it is inherent in the design. Therefore, the behavior of a machine is an appropriate vehicle for analyzing the nature of the man who built the machine.

Chapter Three

Scalpel, Suture, Sponge...Sliderule

*Come now, and let us reason to-
gether......*

—*Isaiah. I. 18*

The engineer was never a stranger to the field of health, however,
he is more involved today than ever before. The sanitary engineer
is working hard to stem the rising tide of air and water pollution;
the electronics engineer is providing devices to help understand the
healthy person and to help cure the sick person; the civil engineer
is working on structures which bring more light, more air, more
water, more room and greater freedom in moving people and products from place to place; the mechanical engineer is developing aids
for the handicapped and power supplements for the well; the
chemical engineer is designing the apparatus to mass produce medicines; and the bioastronautical engineer is investigating the effects
space environments have on man.

But more specifically, there is a new breed of engineer: the biomedical engineer. In essence, the biomedical engineer is trained
and skilled in a composite of the life-sciences and the engineering
specialties. He works with the physician on medical advances and
research, bringing his engineering knowledge and methods to the
biological laboratory and the surgery room. While there are few
biomedical engineers at present, their growing number and, more
significantly, their increasing contributions to the solution of problems in the biological and medical fields, are bringing them to the
public attention. The biomedical engineer is truly a hybrid who has
no precedent in either medicine or engineering.

While a trickle of men are trained specifically as biomedical engi-

27

neers in diagnostic, preventive, and corrective medicine, there is a flood of traditional engineers who are becoming partners on biological and medical teams; some on a full time basis, but most on a part time relationship. A few engineers join for friendship, others for interesting diversion, and some are almost forced by medical people who are desperate for their talent and knowledge.

To cite a few examples, a retired engineer whose hobby for years has been designing, first developed an electromagnetic and then a pneumatic driven dybological heart for the Artificial Organs Department of the Cleveland Clinic. (This department, incidentally, employs full-time engineers.) Thirty-five engineers of the Illinois Bell Telephone Company have gathered into an informal group called SAVE (Service Activities of Voluntary Engineers). The aim of this group is to develop devices needed in clinical research and therapy at the University of Chicago. In their spare time they have developed a three-ounce device that can count and keep a record of the human heartbeat and which can be worn during a full day of normal activity. Other projects of this group are a computer mechanism to detect membrane disease in infants, a visual/aural electronic stethoscope, and an electronic calorimeter to measure and record changes in body heat. Generally, through the efforts of the types of engineers mentioned above, the stethoscope, the optical microscope, the hand stitching and the like have been giving way to the cathode-ray oscilloscope, the electron microscope and the blood-vessel-stapling machine.

Doctor-engineer cooperation also effects the doctor-patient relationship. To illustrate, an engineer (three offices down from mine and who is also a week-end dirt farmer) suffered detached retinas in both eyes. By discussing his condition with the opthalmologist, he learned that the current damage had been preceded by multiple previous detachments which nature had temporarily corrected. The unique extent of the damage—if it was to be corrected at all— required surgical procedures never before performed. The engineer-patient was invited to be a vocal "Exhibit A" at a gathering of some twenty eye specialists. As the preoperative examinations progressed, the engineer noted that the proposed operation called for a feat in precision engineering in miniature, coupled with a careful statistical study of failure risks.

A small ridge had to be built up at the back surface of the eye so that there would be something onto which the retina could be sewn. This ridge had, mechanically speaking, most of the characteristics of an earthen dam. Stress points, tension force, strength of material (that is, tissue), and so forth were calculated with straightforward engineering structural analysis techniques.

Serving as an engineering consultant to his surgeon, the patient underwent several operations. One involved the unprecedented removal of fluid pockets entrapped between retina layers. In this case the restoration of a blind eye to an unaided 20-30 vision was attributed to mutual understanding and cooperation of a medico-engineering problem.

It is not surprising that the physician and the engineer have joined in a mutual assistance pact; the wonder is that it took so long. However, until recently the engineer did not deal with products approximating human complexity such as a computer or a closed life-support system. It is also relatively recent that the field of medicine has reached a degree of knowledge of the human body whereby complex electronic equipment could be meaningfully applied for its betterment. Even when intellectual exchange was found to be mutually beneficial, the problem of communication between the engineer and doctor often became a barrier. The typical engineer was either not equipped or little inclined to study medical literature and, further, did not know what the doctor needed in the way of new devices. The doctor, conversely, had little idea of the capabilities of the engineer. To further becloud the issue, the reputable physician was sensitive to the past history of medical quackery and charlatanism based on the therapeutic and diagnostic devices of the "magic cure through cosmic magnetic belts" type.

The more doctors and engineers worked together, the more apparent the benefits became. For example, problem areas in each of these applied sciences were frequently similar; a solution for one was often applicable to the other. To illustrate, there was a high rate of post-operative paralysis in accident cases where the surgeon had to work against time to prevent excessive loss of blood or a serious infection. When the problem was presented to a telephone engineer, he suggested a technique long used in telephone cable splicing.

When a telephone cable was accidentally dug up by a bulldozer or steam shovel, the damage was quickly repaired because the insulation on the wires was color coded and each could be mated with its proper counterpart. The suggestion was made that surgeons use color coded suture cord to tie off blood vessels, nerve endings, and bronchial tubes when cutting into the damaged area. Then the color coding could be used to match the ends of the severed parts. Conversely, in nuclear space power system work, engineers were having difficulty with "crudding." This was a building up of unwanted deposits in the tubes carrying liquid metals to the turbogenerator. The problem was analogous to the clotting (thrombosis) of the blood on the surface of the mechanical hearts implanted in dogs. The Cleveland Clinic was checked to determine methods to solve the problem. One solution was to put an ionic charge on the surface of the tubes to prevent electrolytic attraction of unwanted material.

While there are differences in medical and engineering approaches, it was found that each approach ideally supplemented the other. The engineering field is dominated by theory; the medical field is dominated by practicality, and often empirical approach. The engineer, through study, can explain—mostly in mathematical language—the intricacies of body processes. The physician, on the other hand, provides clues to the engineer for hard-to-solve problems by telling him how nature does it. Needless to say, great benefits can be expected from this collaboration and cross-fertilization.

The communication barrier also stemmed in part from human weaknesses. Medical people complained that the electronics companies do not know enough about the intricacies of human disease and patient care to design new medical products properly. Engineers, on the other hand, were either unaware of the potentialities or were uninterested. To these engineers, the medical doctors worked in a mysterious world of their own. The doctor thought of the engineer as someone who designed bridges or who buried himself in mystifying black boxes full of incomprehensible electronic parts.

I saw these two forces at play during the first interdisciplinary meeting I attended in 1958. The medical student, hired in connection with the work being done on self-repairing machines, suggested such a meeting. He said that before joining our group he had no idea of the specific functions of the engineer. He said he was amazed at the similarities of the problems faced by both engineers and physicians. When he became aware of the common plight shared by the two professions, he offered to arrange a mutual problem-and-solution-exchange type seminar at the State University College of Medicine at Syracuse, which he was attending. But he was not particularly optimistic since a typical reaction to his proposal was: "Why? What have we in common?" More fundamental was our summer employee's thought that the medical people might feel reluctant to discuss with "outsiders" topics in which they themselves were not completely expert for fear their public image would suffer. In any event, the seminar was held and people on "both sides" unanimously agreed that it was profitable and enjoyable.

Although joint cooperative meetings between doctors and engineers were rare in 1958, there is today a strong and growing interchange of ideas between the life scientists and the physical scientists. Further, when medical men and engineers work side by side for a common purpose, each learn a great deal about the other's technology. And furthermore, the unique demands of some of the far-out biomedical projects being investigated generate new research in raw and unturned fields of interest to each discipline.

Precisely how a physician thinks of an engineer and vice versa is expressed well by a man who has spent ten years practicing both professions. There are only a thousand people in the entire world who have training and experience in both medicine and engineering. John F. Davis is of this rare breed and he is also executive director of the International Institute for Medical Electronics and Biological Engineering. He expresses mixed emotions in the following manner:

"When I think of myself as an engineer, I see a doctor working with dark, mysterious forces. The magic of his science disturbs me, and I would like to bring to medicine a more sound physical and logical basis. On the other hand, when I think as a doctor, I imagine that the engineer, for all his miracles of measurement and analysis, fails to appreciate the complexity, the uniqueness of each patient." *

The pioneers in organized biomedical engineering were, understandably, governmental agencies. The Office of Naval Research is considered the oldest group in the field, founded right after the

* "Medical Engineering," John F. Davis, *International Science and Technology*, September 1964, p. 18.

close of World War II. By far the biggest spender in all categories of biomedical engineering research today is the National Aeronautics and Space Administration. The Air Force too has many projects mostly in aerospace and flight medicine. Research in these governmental branches is concentrated mainly in the design of physiological monitoring instruments for astronauts, development of prosthetic devices for amputees, study of man's tolerance to extreme flight environments, and investigating life-support requirements for space systems design. Also, the biomedical engineers in these agencies concern themselves with the design of manned vehicle simulators to test visual perception, auditory perception, skilled motor performance, and the human factors shared by man and machine.

A governmental agency which sponsors research aimed more at the general public is the National Institute of Health, part of the public health service of the U.S. Department of Health, Education and Welfare. The NIH supports about 40 per cent of the health-connected research in this country, a large share of which is directly in the field of biomedical engineering. Comprised of many hundreds of research laboratories located mostly near Washington, D.C. and Bethesda, Maryland, the life scientists have for the past several decades conducted research both for aids to medical practice and in the study of the human body.

The biomedical engineers of the NIH work not only in the traditional fields of medicine and biology, but also in the agricultural sciences, life processes in the voids of space, and at the ocean depths. The NIH clinical center is one of the world's foremost users of up-to-date electronic medical equipment in their operating rooms. For example, they have a panel board which displays a running record of twenty-four physiological readings such as blood pressure, breathing and temperature, plus provisions to record on tape all events of interest that take place from the moment a patient is wheeled in to the time surgery is complete. While fewer than ten per cent of the nation's hospitals can afford the $500,000 price tag to equip an operating room, the NIH clinical center does provide a model—and an experimental laboratory—for the benefit of all.

Beginning in September 1961, Johns Hopkins University and the Universities of Pennsylvania and Rochester offered for the first time, anywhere, a Ph.D. curriculum in biomedical engineering. Also, to provide the medical profession with some much needed engineering help, Drexel Institute of Technology now offers a full-time graduate program in medical instrumentation. This course is designed for both the engineer who knows little about biology, and the physician with no technological training.

The engineers go to school for four semesters, the doctors seven —both taking the same courses the last three terms. After being exposed to one term of biology and medical physics, the engineers are ready for medical-instrumentation work; the doctors attend three semesters of basic engineering principles before proceeding. During the last three semesters, the two groups merge for combined study of measurements, analysis, and control theory as applied to biomedical systems. Students work in small teams comprised of men with varying backgrounds. In addition to classroom work, the graduate students do research on physiological problems at the nearby Presbyterian Hospital.

Perhaps the largest school which conducts courses in biomedical engineering is Northwestern University in Evanston, Illinois. It is the nation's first biomedical engineering center, and is funded by the U.S. Public Health Service. Key personnel include both electrical engineers and life scientists. The school conducts classes at both undergraduate and graduate levels, and draws candidates from many different backgrounds. Among the research programs being conducted at Northwestern are investigations on the way visual images in the eye are encoded into the neural signals that reach the brain; the feasibility of ultrasonic image tubes for looking inside man; electricity as an anesthetic; and on the development of an electronic device which automatically detects defective heart conditions from tape recordings of heart sounds.

Some other institutions devoted to the training of biomedical engineers are: The University of Iowa at Ames, Baylor University at Houston, Case Institute of Technology at Cleveland, and the University of Michigan at Ann Arbor. While only about fifty students were taking biomedical training in 1963, the number is expected to grow as academic facilities are made more readily available. In 1963 the demand for these specialists was fifteen times as great as the supply. Since the Government, either by grants to universities and private research organizations, or through the country's own research agencies, provides most of the funds for medical and biological research, it is natural that the Government is the largest employer of biomedical engineers. However, there is an increasing call for these experts from nonprofit research organizations and several commercial firms who have recently entered this field.

For some years to come, the biomedical engineer will start his advanced training after graduating from the traditional academic engineering programs such as electrical, mechanical, and chemical engineering. Obviously, the biomedical engineer will require a thorough understanding of one—and preferably all—of these engineering disciplines. But he will have to be proficient in the applications of life sciences as well. Currently he has to fit his study of such subjects as biology, physiology, biochemistry, and anatomy into his free time. Eventually, no doubt, a six-year training course, or longer, will be tailored to his general needs. Specialized training will then continue through additional courses or book study, and through practical experience and on-the-job training.

The rapid growth of biomedical engineering is reflected by the proliferation of subdisciplines that has occurred over the past several years. Some examples are: biomagnetism which deals with the biological effects of magnetic fields (who would have suspected that seedlings placed north and south grow more quickly than those placed east and west); biorheology which deals with flow, pressure, and deformation on bone, cartilage, mucus, blood, and the like; biocryogenics which deals with effects of extremely low temperatures on organisms (this is the group which will quick-freeze people dying of incurable diseases and then thaw them out when a cure has been discovered): and still others; biodental, biomechanical, bioelectric, biochemical, biocivil, and so on.

The physician of today already has added electronics to his medical kit in order to prolong the life of and provide relief for his patients. A great deal of electronic equipment is found only in hospitals and clinics because it is too costly for individual practitioners. More reliance is being placed on electronic instruments to observe and accurately measure the motions of a sleeping patient. Another area in which increased emphasis is being placed on electronic equipment is communications in the hospitals. Instead of Dr. Kildare being called for loudly over the public address system— a violation of the "quiet please" sign—the nurse or patient can establish immediate voice contact with the doctor through a small portable radio receiver he carries in his pocket. Hospitals also utilize closed-circuit television. For example, at the Southwest Texas Methodist Hospital in San Antonio, a camera is focussed on a new-born baby in the maternity room and can be seen by the father on a monitor shortly after birth. Television cameras are also being used in surgery to provide medical students the equivalent of a front row seat during operations.

Because of their portability, reliability, and ease of operation, new electronic instruments can be brought into the "field" and operated by non-physicians. For example, electrical engineers at the University of Iowa are developing an automatic heartbeat recorder and analyzer aimed at this usage. Heart records, called phonocardiograms, are taken in less than a minute while the individual is normally dressed. The device listens and records the sounds made by the heart valves opening and closing. The phonocardiograms are then played into a computer which can distinguish between normal and abnormal sounds, and thus uncover many unsuspected heart problems.

With the availability of recently designed systems, patients in hospitals can be "plugged in" to a central computer. Sensors constantly take a patient's temperature, measure his pulse rate, and check his blood pressure. A centralized computer monitors these parameters and when the patient's blood pressure and temperature both decrease—indicating the patient is in shock—a warning bell sounds and a doctor can be rushed to the patient's bedside; saving precious moments and possibly the patient's life. Equipment such as this, currently in use, can help approximately 220,000 of the million heart patients hospitalized in the nation each year who presently die in their beds due to cardiac arrest.

A cardiac monitoring system, costing between $700 and $1,000 per bed, can save an estimated 70,000 lives a year. The cardiac monitor issues an immediate warning at the heart's first irregularity, sometimes even before the patient is aware of it. Speed is necessary when a patient's heart stops beating; a doctor has only four minutes in which to start the heart pumping again before the brain is damaged. The cardiac monitor provides sensors that are wired onto a heart patient; a similar process occurs when taking an electrocardiogram. The circuits travel to centrally monitored communication panels where the conditions of the patient's heart can be observed by nurses. When the alarm device signals any heart irregularity, a heart resuscitation team is alerted. Heart massage has increased the stricken patient's chances of survival by one-third per cent. Under study is the automatic infusion of potent drugs under the control of a computer which monitors blood pressure and flow. Proper dosage will be administered by a closed feed-back loop consisting of a catheter inserted into an artery and a vein to measure pressures in the circulatory system plus a properly programmed computer and an infusion pump.

Several years ago Navy physicians proved that diagnosis was feasible through the aid of long distance telephone lines. The first demonstration occurred several years ago, between the Naval Hospital at Bethesda, Maryland and Kansas City, Missouri, one thousand miles away. The doctors who were attending a convention in Kansas City received information from electronic signals transmitted over the telephone line, after the information was picked up by special apparatus attached to the patient. With a brief history of the patient's symptoms as a supplement, the doctors in Kansas City successfully diagnosed—sight unseen—two heart cases, and a case of diseased kidneys. Each remote-controlled diagnosis took only about ten minutes. The special equipment developed by a group doing research in aviation medicine for the Navy was designed to pick up, for telemetered transmission, a patient's electrocardiogram, pulse, respiratory rate, respiratory volume, and breath sounds. Because this physiological information can be transmitted over radio waves as well as telephone wires, applications in space travel are feasible.

Today quick transmittal of medical data and facsimile material over telephone lines is quite routine. In addition to the type of material mentioned above in the Navy experiment, there are X-ray photographs and electroencephalograms sent from general practitioners in small towns to specialists in clinics and hospitals in the larger cities for analysis. These same telephone lines are also used to handle the doctor's financial bookkeeping. An electronic transmitter installed in the doctor's office is linked to a computer in the bank in which the doctor has an account. The doctor or his aide simply inserts a pre-punched card into the transmitter and records the service given a patient and the amount charged. This information is automatically recorded on the computer in the bank where each day's information is transferred to magnetic tape. From this data patients are billed, statements mailed, daily charges and cash receipts reported, a record printed of outstanding bills, a summary of charges and services given patients, a record of all cash payments and journal entries made, and statements of income and expenses, as well as assets and liabilities. No doubt the computer could prepare the doctor's income tax statement and print out a check for the Internal Revenue Service—but the check would have to be signed by hand.

In addition, computers directly assist the doctor in his medical work. Just as the doctor sends financial data to the bank's computer, he will send patient data to regional medical-information centers. This information includes exposure to X-ray (cumulatively kept for a patient's lifetime), the patient's allergies, blood pressure readings, illnesses, treatments, body frame type, and so forth. If necessary the information can be retrieved quickly in a similar manner as the financial data. Using electronic computers to keep medical records is becoming more and more common in hospitals throughout the land. Detailed information on thousands of patients is fed into computer tapes, and the data gathered from subsequent visits are added later. The computers make written records unnecessary and thereby eliminates the storage problem. They provide instant cumulative data on all patients: their symptoms, checkup dates, and the like.

The immediate availability of medical information alone is a great aid. But the computer's ability is not limited to this type of performance. Some are already being developed which can read X-rays and electrocardiograms. With these additional skills, and the patient's complete medical history, symptoms, and prognoses plus the experience of thousands of other physicians, the computer could, in the future, diagnose almost instantaneously. It might also prescribe the best treatment, and give the odds for successful recovery. If the computer "feels" it is not sure (i.e. doesn't have enough information to make a decision), it could signal the patient to swallow a shirt-button sized FM transmitter which broadcasts electrical activity of the muscles, heart, and respiratory system. (The transmitters have already been used successfully.)

Such diagnostic procedure went into limited operation in 1964 in the neurological section of the Massachusetts Institute of Technology. A CE-225 computer was linked to three Boston hospitals by telephone lines, and data were automatically processed, analyzed, and returned to the hospitals both in graphic and in verbal (via teletype) form for the physicians' use. The data fed into the computer included electrocardiograms, eye movements which are followed by the patient from computer triggered lights, and patient hand-motor-coordination signals. The computer is programmed to detect and report any abnormalities. There are plans to expand this project to include reception and transmission of data of remote diagnoses to medical facilities throughout New England.

Dr. Arthur L. Norins of Stanford University has programmed a computer to diagnose skin diseases. The machine is fed the patient's symptoms, observations, medical history and pathological information from tissue examinations. The computer then provides the most likely description of the disease.

Mental as well as physical conditions can be diagnosed by the computer. The Mayo Clinic has fed thirty years worth of personality tests into an IBM computer to serve as background information. The test as described by W. M. Swenson, clinical psychologist, is based on the Minnesota Multiphasic Personality Inventory to determine personality traits. The test contains a series of "behavior descriptive statements" to which a patient responds true or false. After noting and analyzing the data, the computer prints out simple evaluations like "probably somewhat eccentric, seclusive and withdrawn, many internal conflicts." Incidentally, the program can detect conscious lying, defensiveness, malingering, mental confusion and poor reading ability. To study the relationship between personality types and certain disorders, the clinic is gathering data from patients with rheumatoid arthritis and cardiovascular disease.

The biomedical engineer also will be making a great contribution to medical progress through the application of automation techniques. Routine laboratory processes of the medical, biological, or biochemical researcher readily lend themselves to automation. Automation can also be applied to patient specimen analysis, the monitoring of physiological data from patients under surgery or during recovery, or to the conduct of drug tests mentioned previously. Further, automation can lessen the hazards of handling radioactive or pathogenic materials. Frequently, scientists and laboratory technicians are required to handle radioactive materials, withdraw dangerous fluids by hand, or even suck them by mouth into pipettes. Mechanization of these processes can increase human safety and at the same time provide more accurate, reliable and speedy results.

Many people have accused the medical doctor of being careless, and sometimes haphazard in his diagnosis. Yet, in most cases, he investigates the ailment as quickly and as accurately as he can with whatever information he has been given. While methods for fool-proof examinations cannot be carried in a little black bag, a doctor must be content with tapping, feeling, looking, and listening. And since technology is not providing the means for one hundred per cent accurate diagnosis, the doctor-engineer team is developing an increasing number of new devices to search out disease and abnormal functioning.

Providing the people of the United States with medical care today is a healthy business and one that is expanding at a faster rate than the over-all growth of the national economy. The reasons for the increase include population growth, longer life expectancy, a greater use of private and governmental medical insurance, and the rising standard of living. Because the field of medicine and hospital care now has more to offer—new diagnostic treatment and therapeutic techniques—the public has become increasingly health-conscious. That hospitals have become big business is indicated by their assets having more than doubled in the period 1954-1964 to exceed twenty billion dollars, and new hospital construction running almost two billion dollars a year. Operational expenses alone for these institutions was approximately eleven billion dollars in 1963. In 1964 there were 1,700,000 hospital beds and about 28 million people (one out of every eight) spent time in a hospital. Hospital outpatient visits totaled 188 million. The average patient per day cost, including nursing and meals, rose from $9.39 in 1946 to $38.91 in 1964.

The nation's yearly health bill in 1964 was more than thirty-five billion dollars and it is rising seven per cent per year. Doctors, nurses, orderlies, and others comprise a work force of over two million—equalling those in the steel and auto industries combined. Excluding military and space activities, the medical "industry" is the fourth largest in the United States; with funds of one and a half billion dollars yearly for medical research and another billion of Federal funds for new facilities.

Because salaries for personnel draw a relatively high proportion of the hospitals' budget (7.35 billion dollars for 1.85 million employees) labor saving techniques become quite important. The use of disposable equipment such as syringes and needles, gloves, blood administration sets, scalpels, forceps, catheters, oxygen tents, and dishes does much to cut labor costs, and also reduces the danger of secondary infection. Many of the advanced techniques developed for industry are being applied in hospital management such as statistical charting, linear programming, and machine record keeping. While a good portion of hospital equipment is still of the 19th century vintage, medical instrumentation and facilities are gradually improving. Fortunately, our hospitals are not immune to the beneficial and cost saving trends of automation.

Medical schools, which are preparing the next generation of doctors, and the more progressive hospitals and clinics, are already using advanced data processing techniques and electronic diagnostic and therapeutic equipment. Over 500 companies in the United States are in the medical instrumentation field; and biomedical engineering expects to become more than a $1.2 billion a year industry by 1970.

While general mass production of medical electronic devices is still a future development, there is a favorable amount of interest in those items already available. Further acceptance of electronic aids to medicine will depend upon the rate physicians are trained and how readily they understand these instruments. Also, lower cost and easier operability will tend to move medical electronic equipment from the research laboratories and advanced clinics to the patients' bedside in the general hospital. The doctor of the younger generation will have seen the benefits of the new equipment and will possibly use similar methods in his own practice.

In spite of rapid and spectacular developments, medical electronics is not a new area. X-ray and radiation treatment dates from 1895. Electrocardiographs and electroencephalographs were widely used before World War II. But the discovery and development of computers, lasers, transistors, fiber optics and data processing equipment have made the engineer and medical researcher react like small boys in a candy shop—they cannot decide what to choose first. There are innumerable applications for body monitor sensors, hospital support equipment, diagnostic devices, analytic equipment, and therapeutic tools for the treatment of specific diseases and disorders. Yet no one company is large enough to develop all possibilities and none is naive enough to believe that success is guaranteed.

X-ray machines, while important and helpful, do have limitations: there is the obvious radiation hazard; there is little contrast in the X-ray picture; accurate dimensional measurements are difficult to obtain. To solve these three problems and to provide other benefits, a nondestructive test tool widely used commercially is being adapted for medical use. This is the ultrasonic sound wave equipment which may in time rival the X-ray as a means of looking into man. While ultrasonics—as a laboratory curiosity—was known in the 1920's, it was not used until 1940 when Dr. F. A. Firestone of Michigan University produced the first practical ultrasonic flaw detector. His apparatus used small short bursts of ultrasonic waves to obtain reflections from minute defects in materials. The principle is essentially the same as that used in radar. That is, a pulse of energy is sent out from the transmitter and reflected back from a target into a receiver. In this way, the size of the target can be determined along with its distance and direction from the transmitter.

Technically, ultrasonic waves are mechanical vibrations whose frequency exceeds 20,000 cycles per second, the approximate maximum hearing range of the human ear. In practice, however, most commercial ultrasonic testing is done at frequencies between one and twenty-five million cycles per second. Surprisingly, ultrasonic waves are transmitted in straight lines through solid bodies such as steel, and are practically undiminished in intensity even at distances of several yards. This contrasts with X-rays whose penetration is measured in inches.

Among the other uses of ultrasonics is the determination of heredity fleshing characteristics in livestock. The ratio of fat to lean is easily obtained from the live animal since the fat and the lean portion each has its own measurable acoustical characteristics. In fact this method is used to select the prize beef at the Chicago Stockyards. Ultrasonics are also used in therapy for arthritis and similar diseases. For diagnosis, the equipment is used for locating gallstones or kidney stones and breast lesions. Ultrasonic encephalography is used to reveal small density variations in brain tissue. Skull thicknesses can be measured, and the size and location of veins or the heart can be presented on a cathode-ray oscilloscope. Ultrasonic pictures can be taken of unborn babies without any danger of radiation hazards.

An example of a relatively simple electronic device that is a boon to both doctor and patient is the Thyrograph developed by the Tudor Instruments Corporation, Hempstead, Long Island. This device measures the duration of the Achilles tendon reflex which is used to determine the functional state of the thyroid gland. This ankle jerk reflex has proven to be of great use as a screening test for thyroid malfunction and as a simple means of checking the progress of patients being treated for thyroid abnormalities. The Thyrograph consists of an electronic measuring device connected to a pedal which rests against the sole of the patient's foot as he kneels on a chair. When the patient's Achilles tendon is tapped, there is an involuntary sudden contraction of the calf muscle. The direction and duration of the motion caused by the ankle jerk is translated by a potentiometer into electronic signals and recorded on paper tape. The continuous line recording, with measurable blips and depressions, can be interpreted in much the same way as an electrocardiograph. Since the Thyrograph is battery operated, it often replaces the tedious and uncomfortable basal metabolism tests previously used for diagnostic studies.

While the medical electronics field is drawing the practice of medicine into new spheres it will have to adhere to proven practices. The producers will have to work very closely with the consumer. The doctor has little time to experiment and certainly cannot afford mistakes. Yet the doctor must be taught many of the intricacies of engineering design and product production. The doctor must "know" his equipment in as great detail as he does his patient; there is variability in each. On the other hand, the engineer must learn to speak the doctor's language and to understand his methods, problems, and limitations. But the results will more than justify the effort. The field has enormous potential not only for monetary gain, but for the promotion of humanitarianism on a scale never before possible. Electronics can provide the means to eliminate pain, reduce suffering and rebuild broken lives.

An important function of the biomedical engineer is, of course, to help cure the sick. But he also will participate in the function of prolonging life, postponing old age, and forestalling the onset of decrepitation. It is said that the two things that are inevitable are death and taxes, but is it—death, I mean? The history of mankind certainly supports the validity of the assumption that man cannot live forever. If you examine the progress made in the past seventy-five years you will note an increase in the average life span from forty years of age in 1900, to almost double that today. It is hoped that with the cooperation of the physical and biological sciences, both theoretical and applied, this gain represents only the beginning of a still greater life span. There is no medical research available to indicate that there is a time barrier for man.

Around the time of Pasteur most deaths were caused by bacteria and viruses. People seldom died of old age but rather from tuberculosis, whooping cough, diphtheria, scarlet fever, pneumonia, and the other infectious and contagious diseases. But with the advent of sanitation (for which we owe the engineer a large measure of thanks), vaccines, antiseptics, antibiotics, and so forth, deaths caused by infectious disease dropped sharply. It is only a matter of time until cures are found for the other so-called degenerative diseases such as diabetes, coronary and cerebral thrombosis, and cancer.

Parenthetically, it may be added that violent deaths (accidents, homicide, and suicide) represent a greater percentage of the total cause of death than those due to infectious and parasitic diseases (eight per cent versus seven per cent). In the area of accidents, particularly, the biomedical engineer can make a large contribution.

There are several theories to explain the aging process. One is believed to be an accumulation of metabolic poisons that are not eliminated when new cells are formed. Consequently, when this poisonous level becomes critical, the body can no longer operate. There is also a hypothesis that at birth, a biological clock is set which runs out, after about seventy years. This theory predisposes all efforts to prolong life to failure, but fortunately, not many gerontologists accept this supposition.

The current prevalent theory is that there is a tendency of all organized things to slow down with time. There are even chemical changes in substances such as concrete, rubber, and leather. Stiffness, brittleness, rigidity, cracking, are all typical of the aging process. It is obvious the human body recovers from disease or bodily damage more quickly in youth than in old age which is characterized by less resistance and slower recovery. As an example, the child who has a fever of 105° at two o'clock in the morning, when the doctor is called, is almost back to normal by the time the doctor arrives at three-thirty. On the other hand, the golden-ager who suffers from some "slight injury" may carry the damage, unhealed, for the rest of his life.

This does not imply that the aging process is constant or always in a deteriorative direction. As noted by Dr. Leontine Goldschmidt of the Creedmore Institute of Psychobiologic Studies, man's aging process is uneven rather than consistent. At the transitional ages, of childhood and late adolescence, a person undergoes "aging crises," but he recovers from them quickly. However, during a later crisis, at age 35 for example, recovery is neither as fast nor as complete. For example, during this crisis, red blood cells are destroyed by heat at a rate faster than normal. Yet, there is a temporary reversal of the aging process (with remarkable recovery of blood cells) between the ages of 60 and 70. If the cause of this reversal can be found, it will represent a vitally important break-through— especially if the condition applies to other organs such as the brain.

Yet, it is a mistake to assume that because the average life-span can be increased (as it has by 6.7 years from 1943 to 1964), the problems of old age have been solved. Quite the contrary. More than 74 million Americans are afflicted by chronic diseases. To illustrate, there are 12 million suffering from heart trouble, and another 12 million with arthritis and rheumatism. Three million have diabetes—half of whom are not aware of it. It is knowing what to do with the people who are "saved" that represents the biggest problem to the doctor-engineer team.

Much, if not all, of the body's activity and control processes are closely linked to chemical action. Fortunately, chemical research is more intensive than any other segment of our rapidly accelerating technology. In any event, the biomedical engineer, perhaps better than anyone else, appreciates the complexity of the human body.

While much of this complexity involves cellular growth and repair, muscular movement, digestion, and the like, the highest level of complexity is reached in the body's chemical and nervous control system.

The complex interactions between the body's many regulatory systems are undoubtedly the source of the body's immense power to adapt, resist infection, and maintain the internal status quo. This high degree of interaction makes it almost impossible to separate cause and effect. Here the biomedical engineer stands on somewhat firmer ground. Systems theory developed by engineers permits an intelligent attack on the problem. In this connection, systems engineering is one of the fastest growing branches of the discipline.

Thus, the influence of the engineer on medical progress will be considerable, and biomedical engineering developments will continue at a high speed. By developing a common language, which will permit better understanding of all on the biomedical engineering team, contributions from many engineering specialists such as fluid dynamicists, rheologists, automation and control engineers, electrical and electronic engineers, chemical engineers and structure-analysis engineers can be made. All will find a wide field of application awaiting them to help increase longevity, decrease the death rate, alleviate pain and discover cures.

There is no doubt that today the physician is the senior partner in the doctor-engineer venture and he may always remain the titular head. But in time the engineer will rise to be at least the power behind the throne. Why will this happen? Because there is a contrast between the driving, objective, logical and often cold disposition of the engineer and the general lack of mathematical training of the physician, the lack of precision and descriptive depth of their language, and the empirical approach of their techniques to solve medical problems. To those who question these differences between engineer and doctor, I suggest a side by side comparison of the traditional sketches of the body's heart system found in medical text books with equivalent "schematics" and "blueprints" of engineering diagrams of the same cardiovascular system.

When engineers performed only in the field of engineering to design and build bridges, dams, highways and so forth, their performance lacked public interest. It is doubtful if more than several persons in a thousand could name even one famous engineer, either living or dead.

Slowly, however, the engineer was called upon by the businessman to help lay out manufacturing plants to efficiently use the machine tools the engineer had designed. The engineer subsequently was asked to set productivity standards and formulate the most efficient production schedules. He then went to work for the businessman directly in designing new products to be made on the machines; to sell the products because only the engineer could fully understand them; and to supervise the employees because of the high technical content of the work. But once in management, the engineer found that he wasn't quite as well equipped to handle people-problems as the graduate from a business school.

Still, this proved to be only a temporary setback. For with the advent of data processing and computer-aided decision making, complex business techniques such as linear programming, systems theory and statistical analyses, plus efficient planning tools such as Program Evaluation and Review Technique (PERT), Critical Path Methods (CPM) and advanced costing procedures—all of which lend themselves beautifully to computer handling—the people-problems all but disappear simply because the people themselves disappear. As a consequence scientific and technical people are found heading almost half of the top management positions in the United States. And if current trends continue (the number of scientists and engineers growing at a rate four times higher than that of the labor forces), key industrial corporate positions will be essentially one hundred per cent occupied by scientists and engineers before the turn of this century.

The foregoing, by way of presenting a precedent, should not in any way be construed as being an insidious Machiavellian usurption of something rightly belonging to another. Put simply, the engineer didn't assassinate the businessman—he *became* the businessman.

Immediately the reader may feel that this was inevitable for business, as indeed it was. But is such depersonalization as the engineer effects possible—or desirable—for something as personal as one's own health? To this I answer that depersonalization of the doctor-patient relationship has already been initiated by the physician.

The traditional role of the family doctor is changing, being forced into a new and sometimes uncomfortable pattern. The familiar

image of the family doctor is one of friend, counselor, and com-
forter—not as much through medicine as by his presence. The
general practitioner felt a warm personal regard and concern for
his patients and gave the feeling that he was treating people, not
illnesses. The family doctor reigned supreme when cities were much
smaller than they are now. He maintained the tradition of individ-
ualized and personalized concern of one man for the health and
well-being of another.

But as our cities overgrew into the suburbs and small towns became large cities, the general practitioner was joined by specialists
such as obstetricians, surgeons, and pediatricians. He not only lost
his patients to the specialty practitioners, he lost his freedom to
practice among the patients he still had. Surgical and obstetrical
privileges were restricted more and more by hospitals. The medical
procedures he had once undertaken as a matter of course were
suddenly barred to him. Even if he dared undertake advanced medical practices, at his own risk, he did so knowing that other doctors
in the community were, at least technically, better qualified.

Of course, the general practitioner could and did make a valiant
effort to keep from being completely circumscribed and limited.
Many medical schools have organized and encouraged excellent
refresher programs and training courses designed to keep the con-
scientious general practitioner up-to-date in medicine. But even at
best, medicine has become an overwhelming field for any one man
to master in its entirety. In this light, it is easy to understand why
the number of general practitioners in the United States is decreasing—from 97 per 100,000 persons in 1931 to only 40 per 100,000
in 1964.

The trend today is towards group practice. Even in rural areas
medical groups have set up clinics in small attractive buildings;
doctors pooling their equipment and medical resources. While
many grieved the passing of the traditional family doctor, the highly
expert—but oftentimes impersonal—business-like medical care does
include the use of most scientific techniques for diagnosing, preventing, and treating illnesses.

These medical groups are often founded and organized by general
practitioners as a two- or three-man partnership and possibly growing to include an internist, obstetrician, and a surgeon. In this way,
they become true clinics, often expanding further to include a

radiologist, an orthopedist, as well as representatives of other spe-
cializations. Instead of examination and treatment in a doctor's
private office, today's patient is more likely to visit his doctor in a
small clinic or hospital. There the doctor can call on more trained
personnel to assist him. Also, the increasing cost of medical equipment can be shared by and made available to many doctors. Thus
while the cost of medical care will still increase, so will its effectiveness.

New patient-doctor relationships are being formed. In group
practice there is still an attempt to retain a close family doctor-type
relationship. Difficult cases are invariably attended by two or more
doctors, and patients are comfortable knowing that at least one
doctor is always on call night and day should an emergency arise.

The foregoing discussion does not aim at showing "who comes
out ahead" in the doctor-biomedical engineer-patient relationship.
It is merely to point out one more example of man's passing from
a biosphere into a dybosphere.

Chapter Four

Repairing the Mechanical Man

> *Then the eyes of the blind shall
> be opened, and the ears of the
> deaf shall be unstopped. Then
> shall the lame man leap up as a
> hart, and the tongue of the dumb
> sing. . . .*
> —Isaiah 35.5-6

Within the current generation a profound development has taken place. Or rather, two unrelated developments have taken place which, when considered jointly, represent another example of the "crossover point" (going from the biosphere to the dybosphere) in man's and machine's history. The developments concern the repair of machines and the repair of man. Prior to the crossover point only a mechanic could repair a machine, and only nature could repair a man. Now, a mechanic can repair a man and nature can repair a machine. Incidentally, the term repair is used in the sense of "remove and replace" and not simply to "patch up."

Before going into detail as to how the medical mechanic—the surgeon—replaces worn out body parts with new artificial counterparts, we will establish a proper standpoint from which to view this development in the perspective of the book's theme. That is, for our purpose here, we must ask what role mechanized surgical procedures and devices play in man's existence. (The role that man plays in the machine's existence is deferred until later.)

Up to this point we have discussed the mechanization of man's environment and, most recently, the mechanization of the diagnostic and therapeutic practices of the physician. Now we will take a giant step into the dybosphere and specifically talk about the mechanization of man. This mechanization may be temporary as in the use of a heart-lung machine during open heart surgery, or permanent as in the case of a heart-pacer implantation, or even a complete artificial heart.

New technology and knowledge allows the surgeon to rebuild the body with transplants of living organs—which will be discussed—as well as wholly man-made organs. Impatient researchers in these areas feel that too much time is required for the development of body remaking techniques. Yet, to the man in the street, the speed of their advancements is rapid indeed. Artificial body-aids which made newspaper headlines a few years ago have now become commonplace. Thousands of lives which formerly would have been lost are now saved through such developments as artificial heart valves, synthetic arteries, and blood-purifying dialysis (kidney) machines. For example, it is estimated that fifty aortic ball valves are being implanted every day in patients throughout the world.

Some devices are too big for implantation, but they are a step in the right direction. Artificial kidneys no larger than a hatbox, being developed for mass production by the Swedish Kidney Clinic, will be available for thousands of people every year.

Of course, many of these new surgical developments are still in the experimental stage and life is "prolonged" not for years but only for weeks or even days. And, as is true of any profound pursuit, there are more questions raised than answered. What effect, for instance, will foreign mechanisms have on the body's nervous system and other organs? Also, will there be psychological changes in the patient? The questions are not always medical in nature. For example, can the manufacturer of a faulty organ-substitute be sued; should these mechanisms be sold at a profit, or should they be distributed at no cost?

A field of effort congenial to the biomedical engineer is biomechanics. Biomechanics deals with the effects of gravity, lifting, pushing, and other forces on a person's body while he is at rest or in motion. Put simply, the parts of the body are studied in much the same way as the parts of a machine. Treating the body as a mechanical device is not a new concept. Descartes, in the 17th century, recognized and pointed out the similarity both in structure and in function between man and machine. Even further back, Aristotle subjected the action of animal muscles to geometric analysis in his writings. Leonardo Da Vinci, a specialist in many areas of art and science, was especially expert in mechanics and the machine-like characteristics of anatomy. Da Vinci wrote extensively on the possibility of manpowered flight. He studied the various parts of birds and insects in terms of their mechanical actions and the function of their various parts. His thinking in the area now called biomechanics is best summed up when he said, "Mechanical science is the noblest and above all others the most useful, seeing that by means of it all animated bodies which have movements perform their actions. . . ."

Alfonse Borelli, in the 1600's, sought to demonstrate that animals are machines in his book, *De Motu Animalium*. In this work Borelli explored the amount of force produced by various muscles. It was his theory that bones serve as levers, and muscles function according to mathematical principles. In this sense, Borelli can be called the father of modern biomechanics.

In the field of biomechanics, engineers have developed instruments and devices to study forces in muscles, tendons, bones and joints, while they are at rest. This work falls under the heading of biostatics. For the analysis of body parts in motion, the principles of biodynamics are used to determine the effects of vibration, impact, and acceleration on body structure and function. Biomechanics is more difficult than the conventional mechanics of engineering because the body parts are not rigid or relatively isolated as are the parts in, for instance, an airplane or a bridge. Further, structural parts such as bones and tendons are seldom, if ever, uniform in their cross section as in the case of a steel girder or steel column. The lack of defined and consistent geometrical shapes makes strength-of-materials testing quite difficult. On the other hand, conventional mathematical techniques are satisfactory for studying the tension, compression, torsion, and bending of structural components in a living animal. Also, conventional testing devices are suitable in most cases to measure such parameters as deflection, stress, strain, and fracture limits.

The biomedical engineer uses the information obtained from the mechanical behavior of the body and its parts for designs in many areas of body reconstruction. For example, he may try to find the proper design of substitutes for lost members or for missing parts such as the replacement of knee joints or the head of the femur.

Or he may apply his talents to design assistive devices for members which are present but which have lost their normal function because of muscular injury or disease. The range of a biomechanical engineer's activity varies from the design of such devices as bone plates, nails, and screws which act as substitutes for broken bones, to the measurement of the mechanical strength of scar tissue.

Among the latest developments in bone and joint replacements is Cerosium, a ceramic material that does not react adversely with the body chemistry. Also there is Silastic, a silicone rubber which can be made in various consistencies and flexibilities to imitate body fat as in the case of a synthetic breast or cartilage in the case of ear and nose replacements.

Biomechanics work with anatomists, physiologists, orthopedic surgeons, general surgeons, and so on to provide safer automobiles and more comfortable seats for the drivers of huge earth-moving machines; to study the adverse effects of radiation on the strength of bones; and to create the best type of headgear to prevent skull injury. Using such substitutes as animals, dummies, and cadavers, the biomechanical engineer determines the behavior of the pelvis and spine under static, repeated and impact loading in bending and compression. With this knowledge, he is equipped to better design the machines and vehicles which man is called upon to operate and maintain.

An active area of biomechanical research is concerned with the study of arthritis. This research requires instrumentation to determine the physical conditions within the cartilage of a diseased joint as compared with those of a healthy one. Researchers now have devices for studying changes in the surface characteristics of cartilage through measuring the friction in the joint of an experimental animal. While this test is being conducted, the joint simultaneously can be treated with synthetic biological fluids to determine possible beneficial effects of lubrication on cartilage interfaces. The mechanical properties of arthritic bone are compared with the properties of non-arthritic bone to establish the effect such properties as bone density and calcium content have on the susceptibility of a person to arthritis. Comparisons of normal and diseased bone, as arthritis advances, are also made so that the effectiveness of various medication and treatment can be evaluated.

The biomechanical engineer approaches his work in much the

same way as does the industrial engineer in the factory. Both seek to find the best working arrangement and procedures for a given task. The biomechanical engineer operates on the assumption that time and motion studies are as relevant to the work of a dentist as to the work of an aircraft assembler. As a result of this approach, several improvements have already been made in the equipment and procedures used in dental work. For example, tools, materials, and equipment controls are located most advantageously for both the dentists and the patient; the dentist's hands are relieved of all work that can be more advantageously performed by his feet or other parts of his body; tools and materials are prepositioned to eliminate searching and selecting; the patient's chair is designed so that the dentist can work alternately sitting or standing; and the motion sequence that requires the fewest movements and the least energy has been established to increase the ease, speed, and accuracy of the dentist's work.

Some day perhaps, people with amputated arms or legs may be able to grow new ones as do some lower forms of animals. Or, in time, surgeons will be able to graft complete limbs from a quick-freeze bank onto amputees. Until then, orthopedic and prosthetic devices are the best alternatives. Artificial limbs to partially rebuild injured ones are not new; they probably date back to antiquity. The dentures George Washington wore were made of wood. Until quite recently, the leather arm terminated in a pointed hook for a hand, and the peg leg were about the best substitutes that could be had. The difficulty endured by amputees or those born with missing or misshapen limbs runs deeper than the obvious physical handicaps. The psychological reactions are often even more detrimental. Confidence can be restored and more than two-thirds of the people outfitted with artificial arms and legs return to productive work.

Approximately one out of every four thousand children born in the United States is missing part or all of one or more limbs. The trend nowadays is to provide children with artificial limbs at the age they would normally use them, rather than wait until maturity. In this way, the children accept the prosthetic devices as part of their own bodies and do not develop the substitution patterns caused by moving about without aids. Fitting handicapped children with artificial limbs early in life helps them develop manipulative skills. For example, disabled children equipped with modern pros-

thetic devices learn to dance, skip rope, ice skate, and draw equally
as well as a normal child.

The ability to overcome a handicap cannot entirely be attributed
to the artificial devices. The human body is surprisingly adaptive
even without them. In a southern province of Luzon, I used to
watch, with fascination, a Filipino who lettered signs and drew
posters. He had no arms from the elbow down. He used no aids or
equipment other than the tools normally employed by a sign painter
and yet the quality of his work equalled professional standards.
(Unfortunately, this example represents the exception rather than
the rule.)

Much work has been done in the cosmetic aspect of prosthetic
devices. Artificial hands have been covered with plastic skin which
is complete with natural-looking, painted veins. The fingers on
these artificial hands can be operated by muscles of the forearm or
biceps. Yet, for the present, a person has to decide whether to have
a natural-looking hand limitedly articulated or the more functional
but less attractive mechanical hooks.

An orthopedic arm-aid has been developed by the joint efforts
of biomedical engineers at Case Institute of Technology, and doctors at Western Reserve University and Highland View Hospital
of Cleveland, Ohio. The research device was designed to find more
effective ways to help persons who have little or no capability of
using their arms. This arm-aid for persons handicapped by paralysis,
for instance, is externally powered by high pressure carbon dioxide
capsules and electronically controlled through prerecorded and
stored computer programs. A number of such programs stored on
magnetic tape, which faithfully reproduce human hand and arm
motions, are continuously available for immediate use. This system
allows a person, who does not have the strength or a nervous system
capable of performing useful arm motions, to eat, shave, and read.

Once a program is selected by the patient, the activity of the
splint can be controlled by four eyebrow movements which activate
delicate switches glued to the forehead. For example, raising both
eyebrows stops the movement of the arm in an emergency, blinking
the right eyebrow moves the arm forward into the next part of the
activity, twitching a shoulder muscle activates electrical devices
which move the fingers into a grasping position. To work the splint,

the patient begins by directing a beam from an infrared light source mounted on spectacles he wears to one of several photocells mounted on the arm splint. This selects the desired taped program. By lowering his right eyebrow, the patient gives the splint a forward command. Through these and other actions the patient can eat an average hospital meal in as little as a half hour. The programs for the separate daily activities are prepared by moving the splint through a series of desired motions and having the motions recorded on tape. While all of the controls on this device are external to the patient, new studies of the neural-muscular system are being undertaken in muscle stimulation or mechanical control using bio-electric signals from the body.

This promising development in the area of prosthetic devices is called electromyography, and involves the measuring of velocity and direction of electronic signals generated with muscle contraction. Through pattern-recognition techniques, these control signals can be used to operate devices which assist (orthotics) or replace (prosthetics). Current day technology allows the miniaturization of these pattern-recognition circuits into control packages not much larger or heavier than a hearing aid. However, the problem is not as much with the control subsystem as it is with finding efficient power actuators for the artificial limbs. Electrical pick-offs embedded in muscle fibers or electrodes placed on the skin surface above key motor points can generate electrical potentials from muscular activity. In this way, direct biological control from the body can be substituted for the mechanical control of orthotic and prosthetic devices.

Already in the experimental stage at the Harvard Medical School and the Liberty Mutual Rehabilitation Center is an artificial limb activated by thought signals. In an actual demonstration, an amputee had electrodes fastened to the muscles of his arm stump. Seven feet away a powered mechanical arm was mounted on a supporting post. The amputee triggers the mechanism into various arm-like motions simply by the thought of wanting to move the "arm." This thought process initiates bioelectric signals (myopotentials) which are, in turn, fed into a properly programmed computer. The computer can then direct the type of arm movements (flexing, turning, hand clutching, waving) and the degree of dexterity (delicately grasping an egg vs. gingerly grasping a metal bar).

One of the more fertile fields for the biomedical engineer is in developing techniques and devices which will help the blind to read, to work normally, and to move about easily in their daily activity. A very slight start has been made by putting an audible signalling device on a cane which, through acoustic ranging, tells how far away an object is. In almost all cases, however, prosthetic devices will be rejected which are too expensive, too "gadgety," too noisy, or otherwise are more bother than they are worth. Experimenters have succeeded in allowing blind people to "see" flashes of light by electrically stimulating portions of the brain. This development hopefully could at some time in the future lead to a portable seeing-eye through the use of a TV camera.

Not only can the blind be helped, but also persons who have lost their voices through surgical removal or paralysis of their vocal chords. The Bell Telephone Company developed an external mechanical larynx in 1926. More recently, the company has developed an air-actuated vibrating reed which is held snugly against the throat. Sound is introduced into the vocal tract and words are formed by normal movements of the lips, tongue, teeth, mouth, etc. The electronic larynx, which looks like an elongated electric razor, produces a speech volume equal to that of a person speaking at a normal conversational level, though the sound is a bit fuzzy and mechanical. Nevertheless, users of the new battery powered artificial larynx can achieve sentence intelligibility of 97 per cent or more, depending on their experience. The frequency of this device can be adjusted to correspond with the normal range of pitch of a man's or woman's voice. By using a finger-operated combination push-to-talk switch and inflection control, the person can vary the pitch of his artificial voice, thus giving his speech a natural sounding quality previously unobtainable. These devices are far from perfect, but when it is realized that the loss of the power of speech can completely disrupt one's ability to lead a normal life, or earn a livelihood, it is easy to overlook the drawback. As is the case with artificial aids in general, they not only help a person take his place in society and lead a more normal life, but they also are used for research in the normal organs they replace.

Mechanical body-aids are not limited to the limbs or to the organs of speech, sight, and hearing. Major body functions have been successfully taken over by machines. For example, aside from trans-

less to say, ease of operation and reliable control devices have to be an integral part and an important consideration in the design. These extracorporeal machines are primed with twenty-two pints of blood—equivalent to the body's full supply. The machine meters the flow of blood and the amount of oxygenation until the plastic tubes serving as temporary blood vessels are removed and the arteries and veins safely reconnected to the patient's natural heart. With the use of this machine, damaged heart valves can be replaced with synthetic plastic valves and damaged heart walls repaired. In certain kinds of brain surgery, doctors can deactivate the lungs and the heart, confident that the machine will do the blood pumping and breathing for the patient.

There have been several electronic instruments developed recently for eye surgery. As an example, a laser beam (amplified and focused light) retina welder repairs certain types of torn or detached retinas by "spot welding" the damaged membrane back into place. Burning is accomplished with one-thousandth of a second, or less, bursts of coherent light. As the burn heals, heat scars form a bond. The eye surgeon shines a narrow laser beam into the eye from the front (conventionally, an electrode had to be inserted through the back or side) without any risky penetration of instruments. The patient needs no anesthetic and may, if all goes well, get up from the operating table and go home.

Laser equipment is small and quite uncomplicated. The first lasers (laser is an acronym for "light amplification by stimulated emission of radiation") were synthetic crystal ruby rods polished and silvered on both ends and were the size and shape of a pencil stub. A source of intense light such as a photographic flash gun sets the laser into action by "exciting" the atoms of the crystal. As the atoms calm down, they emit tiny packages of light energy (photons) which shoot off in all directions. However, the few photons which hit one polished end square-on then start to bounce back and forth along the length of the crystal rod. These in turn induce the emission of still further photons, thus creating a sort of chain reaction. When this state builds up to a high level, the crowd of photons emerge from one end (which is slightly less silvered than the other end) as a burst of brilliant red light several billion times as strong as the midday sun. It is easy to see how this energy, which can be focused on a spot one-hundred-thousandths of an inch wide, has found wide application in surgical repair.

Another instrument, which uses ultrasonic waves, was developed by Dr. Nathaniel Bronson II in Philadelphia's Smith-Kline Instrument Company. While objects of iron or steel that were embedded in the eye can be removed electromagnetically with relative ease, non-magnetic materials such as brass, silver, and copper pose a problem. With an ultrasonic radar-like device worked from outside the eyeball, the surgeon is able to approximate the location of the object. The tip of the probe emits ultrasound pulses and then picks up the echos returned from foreign objects in their path. The time difference between pulse and echo displayed on a tiny oscilloscope indicates the distance from the probe's end to the object. Attached to the end of the probe is a tiny forceps which can grasp the object for removal. With this ultrasound device, fragments of nonferrous metals, glass, and plastic can be located and removed from practically any part of a patient's body.

A relatively simple, but highly precise, surgical instrument is the hair-shooting air gun. The gun makes possible a form of surgery not available before to treat the condition of aneurysm. An aneurysm is a delicate sack of blood which can form in any artery of the body; something like a bulging inner tube in a weakened automobile tire. In the brain's arteries, they are generally located at the base of the brain, and involve only a single large vessel. After the symptoms of this type of aneurysm (severe prostrating headache, stiff neck, and signs of blood in the cerebrospinal fluid) have aroused suspicion, diagnosis is usually confirmed by an X-ray examination, using a suitable dye in the arteries. In the past, aneurysms have been treated by the application of a tiny v-shaped clip around the neck of the sack. Unfortunately, closure of the clip around the pulsating neck of the aneurysm sometimes ruptured the artery at that point causing hemorrhaging that resulted in either paralysis or death.

Two researchers at the National Bureau of Standards discovered in 1960 that mammalian hairs would cause thrombosis (clotting) of the blood. With this information, H. P. Hegemeyer of the Naval Research Laboratory, designed a pencil-like air-gun to shoot a hair into the aneurysm. Pneumatic power for the gun is provided by a portable compressed-air tank, attached to the gun by a flexible plastic hose. The gun is loaded with a sterilized ¼-inch shaft of hog hair or horse-tail hair. After the aneurysm is exposed by operation, the surgeon places the nozzle of the gun against it, an assistant opens a compressed air valve on signal, and the gun shoots a hair into the aneurysm. Impact and penetration are so gentle that the aneurysm hardly moves. The aneurysm starts to clot up solidly within hours after the operation (called pilojection). Eventually, scar tissue invades the clot and the aneurysm disappears entirely.

Our exploding technology already has brought home to the engineer an ironic fact which is now becoming apparent to the physician —the rapid obsolescence of a new "device or technique." While aneurysms were treated by pilojection in the early 1960's, it now appears that these weak places in a blood vessel can be simply reinforced by a plastic coating. This new method (developed almost concurrently with pilojection) was pioneered by Dr. Bertram E. Selverstone, Professor of Surgery at Tufts University. It requires the use of an airbrush to spray a latex coat over the artery, and drying it with helium.

In the past, the surgical treatment of Parkinson's disease required the precision placement of electrodes in human brain cells only a few microns in diameter. This required many hours in the operating room. After finding the desired location, the stimulating electrode had to be removed and a lesion-maker inserted into the identical position. This position represented the center within the patient's brain controlling the trembling motion characteristic of the disease. Recently a new biomedical engineering design of the probing and lesion-making system proved successful and greatly reduced the time-absorbing, meticulous surgical process used previously. The lesion-making probe has been combined with a depth electrode in a single miniaturized instrument. As part of this newly developed surgical aid, a sterotaxic device that allows a three-dimensional view of things has been developed for the precise placement of electrodes. This allows a major part of the procedure to be handled outside the operating suite in the X-ray room.

Almost every day it seems that new devices and instruments are being engineered to help the surgeon in his work. Among them are electrocautery, to prevent bleeding during surgery; several methods of electronic anesthesia, one of which allows the suppression of pain by an individual who can send weak currents of electricity from a cigarette-size box into a particular portion of his brain, through embedded probes; electronically controlled streams of sterile air, that flush a wound as the scalpel cuts; and infrared detectors which disclose abnormal tissues by the difference in temperature from surrounding normal tissues.

Laser beams have been used to drill holes and coagulate the edges of holes in blood-vessel grafting. And mechanical engineers in Russia, Japan, the United States, and Canada have contributed to the development of stapling devices for blood vessels. Previously, during an operation, surgeons had to sacrifice some tiny blood vessels by cutting them off. Today, tiny blood vessels—especially around the heart, eye or ear—can be mended by threading these severed blood-vessel ends over mandrels and inserting staples in them.

General Electric has made searching for metal objects in the stomach a relatively simple operation. They have developed a steerable magnet which consists of a magnet permanently attached to a stiff spring. The spring, in turn, is attached to the end of a stainless steel cable. A control cord limits the extension of one magnet corner, thereby forcing the stiff spring to bend when the cable is extended. While looking through a fluoroscope, a doctor can easily guide the magnet into a position without damaging surrounding tissue. General Electric's magnet is so designed that it can be shielded, thereby cutting off the magnetic field. If the object being removed becomes lodged—as could an open safety pin—it can be turned around for easy removal with a combination of switching and maneuvering. Some of the items that have been successfully removed by the GE-developed magnets are a padlock, a coffee can key, pins, hypodermic needles, and metal toys.

In complicated surgical situations the procedure is not always as simple. For example, the anesthetist must know the condition of body functions—heart rate, temperature, blood pressure, respiration, the concentration of gases in the patient's lungs. To monitor these functions, and many others, the patient is "wired" and soon resembles an aircraft engine undergoing tests in a well-instrumented laboratory. The wires may interfere with surgery, and in post-operative cases restrict body movement. Serious damage can result if they are accidentally torn out. Here the biomedical engineer utilizes astronautical and meteorological information and has proved that the means to an effective and efficient way of presenting body information is through wireless telemetry.

In this instance, a combination sensor and FM radio transmitter can be swallowed like a pill and steered by strong magnetic fields to any desired part of the stomach or intestines. The Weizmann Institute in Israel has developed a permanent magnet attached to a plastic container which can carry drugs, or possibly a radio transmitter. Once inside the body it is exposed to an outside alternating magnetic field. In this way the plastic container can be kept either in one precise spot within the body where the drug is to be released, or it can be allowed to tumble, turn, and twist its way down through the gastrointestinal tract relaying vital information in much the same way as a meteorological balloon reports temperatures, pressures and other vital findings through its radiosonde as it climbs into the atmosphere.

There are problems of monitoring and measuring the activities of humans in situations other than surgical. For example, toxicologists evaluate new drugs by giving a subject graded dosages, measuring the degree and duration of sedation (or excitation) and later comparing the changes in activity with that of a control group who have not received the drug. This "activity" may take the form of sleeping, breathing heavily, scratching, quivering, jumping, climbing the walls of a cage (when an animal is the subject) or the neatness and precision with which a spider builds his web (if a spider is the subject). Because of the long duration and the large number of subjects involved, individual observation is almost impossible. Consequently, various devices are needed to measure and record the type, number, and duration of motions during the time intervals. Much of the work done in industry to monitor electronic equipment during life tests on components such as relays or television sets can be applied here. In these industrial tests, thousands of units are placed in operating configurations. The key functions of the components to be monitored are wired to sensing and recording devices which, in turn, are fed directly into a computer. In this way, millions of bits of information are stored for ready use and analysis.

The thermodynamicist is playing an increasingly important role on the biomedical engineering team. Through his participation organic matter or viruses are cryogenically preserved at ultra low temperatures in their natural state for subsequent examination. Also, local spots in the brain or nervous system are cooled, allowing temporary halting of localized brain functions without permanent harm. Removal of the cold source permits restoration of the brain's function.

The trend toward greater mechanization of humans is seen in the direct functional restoration by man-made devices. Although organic parts such as corneas, arteries, and teeth are kept in refrigerated banks to be implanted when needed—complete organs have been transplanted successfully—the supply of these natural parts never meets the demand. They are often diseased or deteriorated, and in many cases are rejected by the patient's body.

In any event, the need increases daily to replace worn and defective body parts caused by accident, infection, paralytic injury, or degenerative tissue. Rather than provide external substitutes or aids, we know by logic alone that duplicating nature as closely as possible is preferable. To illustrate, eyeglasses were originally hand-held lorgnettes, then the style improved to spectacles and then advanced to the more popular contact lenses. The next step—surgically implanting corneas (the clear membrane that covers the pupil) directly into the eyeball—has already been accomplished at the Cedar-Sinai Medical Center in Los Angeles.

Another example of this trend to "build-in" is a recent development from England referred to as an "oral vibrator." You will recall that the Bell Telephone speech-aid was hand-held against the throat. The English device is built into an artificial palate in the mouth or into an upper denture where a tiny electromagnetically vibrated diaphragm is attached to a flexible cable passing out of the corner of the mouth to a small power box carried in a pocket. Pushing a button on the control box starts the diaphragm vibrating and enables the wearer to speak.

Still another example of the trend from external to internal mechanization is the cardiac pacemaker. This device is a special stimulator which feeds timed electrical pulses to the heart, or to the nerves leading to the heart, and results in the heart beating at regular intervals, even though the body's natural heart pacer is inoperative or erratic.

Starting in the early 1950's, pacemaking signal devices have followed a trend typical of similar artificial aids. For five or six years, console-sized electronic pacemakers were used in hospital operating rooms or adjacent to the hospital beds. The patient with his heart beat permanently protected by this immobile electronic device was literally tied to his bed.

Later a portable electronic pacemaker—weighing two pounds and the size of a small book—was designed to send three to five volts of electricity through the disabled heart at a rate of eighty times a minute. A stainless steel braid catheter was inserted through a vein at the neck and followed the intricate path of the circulatory system into the heart. In the early 1960's, the pacemaker was reduced to about the size of a cigarette package through transistorized circuitry. This also enabled pulsing to be adjusted anywhere from sixty to one hundred and eighty beats per minute. Mercury-cell batteries powered the device and operated up to five years before the battery had to be changed. Because the body tries to reject wires passing through the skin, the pacemaker is buried beneath the surface. Consequently the patient must have an operation to replace a battery, the life of which is limited from a few months to a year or more.

The next step is to have the pacemaker powered directly from the body. Experiments are currently being conducted to enable mechanical movements of the body's internal organs to generate electricity. George F. Myers of Bell Laboratories, and Victor Parsonnet of Beth-Israel Hospital, Newark, New Jersey, have already produced experimental pacemakers powered by transducers which are operated by the mechanical motion heart.

As can be seen, the goal behind the development of this type of device is an artificial replacement of a body organ or function which can be "guaranteed for life." But by the same token, it can also be seen how critical the failure of a single transistor or the loosening of a soldered joint can become. The problem of high reliability of these built-in mechanized devices is the same as insuring the reliability of the electronic devices used by astronauts.

Also successful is the substitution of electrical nerves for damaged organic ones. Dr. Andre Djourno of the Faculty of Medicine in Paris used a magnet wrapped with a coil of fine silver wire to successfully restore the hearing of a totally deaf man. The tiny electromagnet is permanently embedded in living tissue and connected to a nerve. When current is applied, the nerve is excited into action. In early 1957, a tiny coil was placed in the temple muscles of the ear behind the temporal bone of a man who had been totally deaf. This man "hears" words that are spoken into a microphone. After a year of experimenting, he was able to distinguish almost three-fourths of the words spoken to him.

At the Israel Institute of Technology's Technion, research is being conducted on patients where the damage is entirely in the ear and where the auditory nerves are intact. Dr. Franz Ollendorff is working on methods for feeding the electrical energy output of a radio amplifier directly into these nerves. Dr. Ollendorff also believes that in cases where auditory nerves have been damaged, the waves from the amplifier can be impressed directly upon the hearing center of the brain by means of electrodes placed against the skull. In a similar development, Dr. Yu I. Sokolovsky writes in his book, *Cybernetics of the Past and Future* (published in Russia in 1959) of using camera devices similar to a television lens which, through electronic impulses transmitted to the brain, will enable the blind to see action, color, panoramic vistas, and so on.

The heart has always held special sentimental meaning to man. It was supposedly the seat of our emotions (heartbroken, lost my heart, heartache, learn by heart, etc.) and the source of our moral strength (lionhearted, stronghearted, heart quaking, good at heart, etc.). It is significant that for many people this treasured organ may be replaced by its dybological counterpart in the near future. Heart valves and sections of heart walls already have been mended by using mechanical parts.

The performance of the human heart is almost unbelievable. It beats about one hundred thousand times a day or about forty million times a year. During an average lifetime, the heart pumps approximately 264,175,000 quarts of blood through the blood vessels of the body.

In the late 1950's Dr. Kolff and his staff began to design and build an artificial heart small enough to fit into the chest cavity, yet as powerful as a natural heart. The first experiments were performed on dogs, who were kept alive by artificial implanted hearts for periods up to twenty hours. Dr. Kolff's next subjects were calves whose weight and circulatory system approximates that of an adult human, and are less prone than dogs to excessive blood clotting. The calves were kept alive for periods up to 48 hours with the artificial hearts. Death does not occur because the heart is in any way inadequate, but because of the excessive length of time the calf has to be on the heart-lung machine while the artificial heart is being implanted and connected and due to poor venous return.

Early pumps were driven by an electromagnet, with both ventricles in a common rigid housing. This type of drive was temporarily abandoned because of heavy weight, heat production, undesirable shape, difficulty of operative insertion, and the impossibility of fine adjustment. Currently, a pneumatically driven, sack-type of artificial heart is being developed. It does not have the same shortcomings as the early pump although there are some disadvantages—the need for a large energy source and a driving mechanism outside of the body. At the present stage of development, a complicated machine must provide fine adjustments of pulse shape, speed, etc. and give important information as instantaneous flow rate and ventricular movements. Attempts are being made to miniaturize and simplify the driving machine outside of the body. The artificial hearts are made of plastic and are molded in one piece. For practical purposes, the dybological heart is divided in two, one part for the left side of the heart and one for the right. The ventricle is composed of double sacs; a thick outside housing, and a thin inside pumping chamber. Compressed air, blown into the space between the two sacs, compresses the pumping chamber through a side tube that is attached to the middle of the housing. Each ventricle is provided with two sensing coils which indicate the position of the sac and also provide instantaneous blood flow measurements. Caged silastic ball valves and tricuspid semi-lunar valves made of polyurethane have been used.

Since the first heart valve was inserted in 1952, many types—flap, bi- and tricuspid, and ball valves—have been fashioned from a number of materials. To work well, a heart valve closes quickly in response to backward flow of blood without impeding the forward flow. It is constructed of materials that neither affect nor are affected by blood and tissue and yet retain strength and elasticity during years of constant work.

The first successful artificial mitral valve was implanted in 1960. In 1963, Dr. Albert Starr of the University of Oregon Medical School (who with an engineer, Mr. Lowell Edwards, developed the ball-type valve) headed a surgical team which replaced the aortic, mitral, and tricuspid valve in a 30-year-old man who, as reported seven months later, was still alive and well. Since this first triple replacement, the Oregon team has made multiple replacements in a number of patients.

Every year almost one million people die from cardiovascular disease in the United States. Some had been suffering for years without the benefit of radical treatment, others die in the operating room during heart surgery. This type of cardiac patient might be a subject for the total replacement of the organic heart with an artificial one. However, great care must be taken before such drastic methods are applied to humans.

Apart from the philosophical considerations attending gross mechanization of people, the growing interest in duplicating the functions of the body brings a whole new set of technical problems. Since many of these new problems are mechanical, electrical, or chemical, they more closely approach the ones associated with industrial research than those of medical science. For example, developing a plastic sleeve to replace a damaged segment of an artery requires engineering knowledge of surface friction, laminar and eddy-flow patterns, pipe wall elasticity, designs for proper hydraulic flow conditions, blood clotting, blood coagulates on different materials, and flexibility in the tubing to avoid kinking.

What will man be like when he becomes more mechanized; or even completely mechanized? Perhaps we should consider a situation from *Alice in Wonderland*. But we would do even better with the *Wizard of Oz*.

Remember the Tin Woodsman? He was in the same predicament. The Woodsman fell in love with one of the Munchkin girls who, unfortunately, lived with a lazy old woman who didn't want to lose a good cook and housekeeper. The old woman, for two sheep and a cow, persuaded the wicked Witch of the East to enchant the Woodsman's axe. Each time the enchanted axe slipped and cut off part of him, the Woodsman went to a tinsmith and had a new part made of tin. Soon he was all tin, but most significantly to him, he had no heart. He could move around as well as ever but with no heart, he lost his love for the Munchkin girl and further, didn't care whether he married her or not. But he considered the loss of his heart the greatest loss of all. After many trials and tribulations (I don't want to spoil the story for those who haven't read the book by revealing the whole plot), the Wizard of Oz cut a square hole in the Tin Woodsman's breast and put in "a pretty heart, made entirely of silk and stuffed with sawdust." Both agreed it was a beautiful heart and, further, the Wizard assured the Woodsman that it was a kind heart, one that any man could be proud of.

The above answer to the question of what a mechanized man would be like could have been put in more "learned" terms, but it couldn't be put more clearly. We know, as did the Wizard of Oz (or the author L. Frank Baum) that a "silk and sawdust" heart is not an exact substitute for an organic heart. But it is a substitute and better than any possible alternative under the circumstances. Still, while technology may not provide an exact substitute, there is no reason to believe it can't provide a "better" substitute in the sense of longer life and greater pump capacity. The problem, however, then arises: What becomes of the Munchkin girl? Perhaps she, too, in her unwed old age will get a substitute heart.

Chapter Five

Men in Space

One machine can do the work of fifty ordinary men. No machine can do the work of one extraordinary man.

—*Elbert Hubbard*

It is an observable fact that man is becoming more mechanized through artificial aids and synthetic part replacement; this is internal mechanization. But it is equally true he is also being mechanized in an external sense through the daily routines of his existence: in his home; his place of work; in his modes of communication and transportation. To an increasing degree, he thinks mechanically, acts mechanically, and reacts mechanically. On the one hand we find mechanical progression; on the other we find natural regression. For better, or worse, mechanization of man takes the form of many spearheads driving deeper and deeper into the front lines of technology.

This is a way of saying that *man himself is a machine,* or at least he can be explained in mechanical terms. It generally takes courage and a sense of humility to admit it, but modern medicine would not exist if a small group of perceptive scientists, in the 15th and 16th centuries, did not have the boldness and the selflessness to realize that man was an integral part of nature. They came to realize that man was not a privileged being and that the universe was not created solely for his exclusive use and enjoyment. They realized—or strongly suspected—that man fitted into the over-all scheme of things in the same way as the plants and animals they were studying.

Subsequent discoveries in elementary mechanics indicated that body parts functioned much like the ropes, levers and grinding mills used in the contrivances being built at the time. In the mid-1800's, with the advent of thermodynamics, it was apparent the human body followed the same principles of energy transformation as the steam engine. With the aid of physicists and chemists, the physiologists broadened their field of inquiry from the mechanics of the body to its energetics. The man-made engine and the man-engine itself were similar indeed.

Yet, with increased knowledge of the body's constituent elements, came a false feeling of smugness and a tendency to oversimplify body mechanics and chemistry in the 1920's. Writers for the Sunday supplements used this knowledge to note with delight the average man's body contained enough water to fill a ten-gallon barrel; enough carbon for 9,000 lead pencils; enough iron to make a six-penny nail; enough lime to whitewash a chicken coop, and the chemicals in the body could be bought (at 1939 prices) for fifty-eight cents. However, I do not recall these writers pointing out that the fifty-eight cents worth of chemicals could be so wondrously arranged at such a low figure.

Perhaps it was only when more complex machines were developed that the incredible intricacies and delicate balance of the human mechanism were realized. Man may be a machine, but he is also an amazing chemical plant, communicator, inventor, artist and philosopher. Of course, understanding the intricacies of the human body requires a great deal of training. For there are more than just straightforward mechanical and chemical aspects to learn. There are the brain and central nervous system involving some remarkable intellectual energy and sensing processes. Consequently, while man can be explained in terms of mechanics, chemistry, information theory, and so on, he likes to feel there is some vital spirit, apart from the physical being, that makes him what he is. Whether or not there is a vital spirit cannot be answered here. However, the conflicts generated by such a belief will be examined presently.

Because of this feeling, most physicians consider a patient's emotional reaction before giving him any clinical details of his ailment. This often presents a problem. The doctors would prefer the patient take the prescribed medication without question, get the proper rest, and "let the doctor do all the worrying." This is the warm approach that has characterized the doctor-patient relationship for many years; it is the "human" approach. In his training, the doctor is taught the importance of treating his patient with TLC—tender loving care. But developing the proper bedside manner is only a fractional part of his training; the most important being the proper mechanical treatment of the human body.

In other words, the average patient is getting the benefit of two kinds of treatment: humanistic and mechanistic. To keep the medical student from being confused by these diametrically opposed "treatments"—which, in principle, they are—he is warned of the dangers of adhering to a complete belief in the principle of *teleology*. This principle is related to the doctrine of "vitalism" which states that the life in living organisms is caused and sustained by a vital force that is distinct from all physical and chemical principles. The medical student is cautioned to concern himself with the *what* and *how* of human phenomena, and to leave the *why* to the philosophers. In agreement with this, the "mechanistic theory" was chosen to be the basis of modern medical training. With regard to life, this theory maintains that all phenomena can ultimately be explained in terms of physics and chemistry, and that the difference between the organic and the inorganic is only in degree.

While the medical student is instructed to treat the patient as a human, and the patient's body as a machine, to my knowledge the engineer does not receive comparable training. A comparison of the ancient development of both disciplines also reflects their different emphasis.

In ancient times, the primitive antecedent of the present-day physician—the witch doctor—adapted a vital theory almost 100 per cent. That is, he treated primarily the spiritual aspects of his patient's problems; the "life force" that was neither chemical nor physical. If his patient was sick, the witch doctor would claim that the patient angered one of the gods. The treatment, obviously, consisted of an appeal to this god through magical incantation. (If the patient survived, the witch doctor took the credit; if the patient died, he would tell the relatives that the patient had angered the gods too much to expect any mercy.) As time progressed, physical things—herbs and surgery—were added to the treatment. Today, the treatment is predominately physical in nature.

Again in ancient times the engineer provided physical devices for his "customers" with only slight traces of spirituality (perhaps a magic symbol or a talisman to be attached to the device something like the rabbit's foot). But as the designs became more complex, the mechanisms operated faster, and were potentially more dangerous to the "customer." The engineer, therefore, had to be more knowledgeable and more concerned with people. The need for greater understanding of both physical and mental capability generated another breed of engineer, the human factors engineer.

The human factors engineer is sometimes concerned with selecting and training the right man for specialized machines, such as spacecraft, but mostly with modifying the machine to fit the man. The man is not the human factors engineer's client, however. The man is either "Mr. Average" in the case of consumer goods or "Mr. Special" in the case of an astronaut. Generally, the human factors engineer considers the operators of automobiles, electronic consoles and powered lawn mowers quite standard. His problem, mainly, is providing enough adjustment in things such as seat height, foot controls, and rear-view mirrors to take care of the variable measurements of people.

In any event, there is little or no personal relationship between the human factors engineer and the man-machine relationship which is to be optimized; the trend is toward an even greater impersonality. The more advanced systems of production and program control seem to grind the "man" down to about the size of letters in alphabet soup. These project planning and scheduling techniques are invariably computerized, with each portion of a complete task broken down into the smallest practical segment. In this way, the cost and time factors of every resource can be kept under scrutiny, and action can be taken when something, or someone, appears to threaten the schedule or budget.

Let me quote from a technical presentation which deals with the "Percent Utilization" of individual skills and the measure of relative cost/schedule efficiency of a program:

"If we wish to be very callous, and for the purpose of an inanimate type of presentation such as we have here, we shall be callous, we can consider that a man and a facility such as a vibration machine, are one and the same. To the computer, they are identical. The only difference is their symbol, and the computer has no feelings of emotion whatsoever. Therefore, as you can see, the manpower analysis in front of you, by merely changing the symbolization, is also a facility analysis. It would be very simple to take the letter 'A,' and rather than say that 'A' is John Jones, we can say

that 'A' is a random noise shaketable. Therefore, I am sure you
realize that when one has programmed the manpower aspect, it
becomes relatively straightforward to handle the facility aspect."

Cold blooded? Yes. Inhuman? Not necessarily. The calloused
"symbol assigner" just quoted may be a very close friend of John
Jones. They may play golf together, they and their wives may be a
foursome at bridge, and they may be old school chums. Yet, if the
job is to get done, John Jones must be treated symbolically—as a
letter of the alphabet. But it must be emphasized that this is for
purposes of computer programming only. No one is in any way
diminished by the process. In a similar manner clear thinking people
realize that they are not being diminished when they are assigned
a postal ZIP number; a seemingly endless telephone number; and a
hard to remember social security number.

The astronaut too must be treated "by the numbers," or he will
never get to the moon or Mars and return safely. He can serve as
a guide for our journey into the dybosphere, for in general what is
true for him today will be true for the rest of us tomorrow. The
astronaut passes—almost visibly—(as he crawls into his space vehicle) the "crossover point" demarcating the biologically oriented
world from the machine oriented world.

In planning for manned orbiting laboratories, lunar landings, and
interplanetary travel, experiments must be designed and scheduled.
These experiments provide procedures, and techniques; they lead to
reliable equipment and facilities; and answer questions about man
never before asked. For example, how does a person respond to long
periods of weightlessness? What are the effects of prolonged confinement, inactivity, artificial atmospheres, radiation and fatigue?
How does man react in strange environments? Is there any limit to
how drastically man can be modified?

To answer these, and related questions, programs have been organized for space experimentation and facilities have been built
throughout the country for environmental studies in space-simu-
lated laboratories. Some studies are relatively easy to develop and
can be conducted on the ground. These include the simulation of
vibration, acceleration and deceleration experienced in blast-off and
re-entry by means of shaker tables, centrifuges, and rocket sleds. It
is also relatively easy to determine the effects of reduced pressures

and 100 per cent oxygen, and to monitor behavioral and psychological reactions to "artificial" situations. Of course, not all of the necessary information has to be newly assembled. A considerable amount is available from recorded experiences and studies in the area of submarine and aircraft operation; and to some extent, from other countries, with whom vital data are often shared.

It is common knowledge that the body can adapt—within limits —to prolonged periods of inactivity. Most of us have experienced the feeling of dizziness when getting out of bed after a period of illness. It took Gordon Cooper a full day to recover from orthostatic hypertension (dizziness) after he emerged from the Mercury space capsule. Impaired circulation had caused a too rapid pulse as well as lowered blood pressure—a condition similar to that of soldiers fainting after standing at attention for a long time. The Russian cosmonaut, Gherman Titov reported an unpleasant feeling resembling seasickness, whenever he turned his head. This may have been caused by weightlessness or the tumbling of his space capsule. It has taken other cosmonauts seven to ten days to fully return to normal. If prolonged weightlessness causes irreversible effects on the human body, as is suspected, then gravity simulation will be necessary. However, if the conditions resulting from a zero gravity environment are slight and simply alleviated, then the cost and complexity of interplanetary vehicles can be substantially reduced.

While some may feel that exercise will be sufficient to offset deleterious effects of lengthy periods without gravity simulation, almost all agree that the astronauts will have to be "reconditioned" before their return. That is, the body may adapt very well to the weightless state but not be able to satisfactorily cope with the high g-forces of re-entry and the return to normal earth gravity. There is also concern pertaining to the behavioral aspects of sensory perception: psychomotor coordination; judgment and reaction time; and so on. This is limited not only to re-entry but to tasks associated with a space mission such as rendezvous and docking with other vehicles, and the normal system operation and maintenance of the space craft. There are also scientists, who, for one reason or another, feel that those who stay in space for long periods may become quite neurotic.

The astronaut in space lives in a world all his own; a tiny world in the vast, hostile, voids beyond the earth's atmosphere. The known dangers and difficult conditions are staggering; the unknown frightening. Yet, we are confident that designs and techniques will be developed to allow the space traveler to live and function as close to normal for mission success and survival.

The following discussion pertains to manned orbital laboratories and interplanetary space vehicles to be built in the early 1970's. It is anticipated that the crew in these craft will be composed of a pilot, pilot/engineer, physicist, bioscientist, astrophysicist, a maintenance engineer, and perhaps others. It is also assumed that there will be a high degree of cross-specialization and training in order for the crew to share responsibilities.

What can these crewmen expect to find in their space vehicles to help them perform their daily tasks, and to provide for their physical and mental well being? One of the vital requirements is a cabin-atmosphere that provides oxygen. While early space craft contained an atmosphere of pure oxygen, it was hazardous. The danger of fire (always present with pure oxygen) and the problem of lung collapse (atelectasis) under acceleration or periodic artificially induced gravity remained acute. For longer missions, experiments indicate that a 50-50 mixture of oxygen and hydrogen at about half normal atmospheric pressure works well. Ironically, nitrogen-rich atmospheres, as found at sea level, present crewmen with the problem of bends due to rapid decompression.

Providing the necessary gases for breathing is only one part of the difficulty; keeping these gases relatively free of contaminates is equally troublesome. Carbon dioxide has to be removed from the "stale" air and reclaimed into oxygen; odors have to be absorbed; water vapor from breathing and sweating condensed and purified. Perhaps the biggest problem is "outgassing." This is the literal evaporation of tiny bits of a substance (including the dense solids) in the form of gas molecules. Outgassing is a constant process everywhere, and normally is not a problem because of ventilation and the relatively large atmosphere of the earth. But in the tightly closed space vehicle, the contaminates accumulate and pollute the air. The combination of innocuous things as dandruff, material shedded from clothing and the interior of the space vehicle, uncollected whiskers from shaving, and bits of flaked off paint form a poisonous pollution.

The problem of a zero gravity condition is not that man cannot adapt to a weightless state, but that the body adapts too well to weightlessness. To illustrate, experiments indicate that a man immersed in water for several days (to simulate a weightless state) finds that it takes a great deal of will power to leave the tank even for routine tests. And once out, he cannot wait to jump back into the water tank. Aside from the mental effects, some scientists feel quite strongly that continuous weightlessness will tend to turn man into a rather shapeless blob, simply because there is nothing to "keep him in shape." While this is a slight exaggeration, it is true that merely keeping the body erect on earth against the pull of gravity requires expenditure of energy and provides for the distribution of calcium in the bones. Without gravity, the bones do not demand calcium, and because the body cannot store the calcium, it is excreted along with other vital minerals in the urine. Not only is 5-7 per cent of the body's bone content lost after seven to eight weeks, but there is also a strong possibility that kidney stones will form. Because of these and other considerations, artificial gravity environments may be provided.

Man does not live by gravity and air alone, he also requires food—about 1⅓ lb. per day. The astronaut's food is currently freeze-dried and reconstituted by adding hot or cold water to the food package. Both food and beverage are injected by squeezing the contents through a self-sealing mouthpiece. Assuming 25 per cent fat is in the diet, the astronaut gets a little less than 2,500 calories per day. On long space voyages, water will be provided from the reclamation of urine; the condensation of moisture in the space vehicle's atmosphere; and the purification of wash water.

To provide food, water, and oxygen for extended trips—perhaps a year's voyage to Mars—presents further problems. It simply is not possible or feasible to carry the amount of fresh supplies required. Fortunately, there are several possibilities which lead to a completely closed ecological system. In other words, the life cycle on earth can be duplicated on a limited basis. Part of this cycle, for instance, is the plants thriving on the carbon dioxide man exhales, while the plants, in turn, give off oxygen for man to breathe. Having plants and algae on board the space craft not only regenerates the oxygen from the carbon dioxide, but they can be eaten. The fast-growing algae, which is also an excellent source of protein, would be supported by sunlight and human waste, and watered by recycled and purified urine. Recycled and purified urine contains less harmful substances than our city drinking water; and we have always used excreted wastes for fertilizers.

An emergency source of food will be found in the walls, insulation, and other structural material of the space ship. It is planned to make as many items as possible out of dehydrated food pressed into various structural shapes. The crew could munch on these during long flights. Surprisingly, an edible structural material is not a new idea. The ice cream cone is classified in this manner by the Patent Bureau.

Space travel involves "biological rhythm," which is the built-in body clocks that appear to operate on the basis of a 24-hour cycle. For example, at approximately the same time every day our efficiency drops along with our heart rate and blood pressure. Obviously, this biological rhythm must be taken into account in devising optimal individual work-rest schedules for the crew. It has been calculated that for a six-man crew, there would be about four hours of daily work per man. The remaining time would be spent in taking care of his physical and mental needs.

Space for moving around presents another problem. For a long time to come, it is anticipated that each man will have only the minimum amount of living space, roughly 250 cubic feet. Under zero-g conditions, the astronauts will have to learn new methods of performing work and moving from one point to another. The exercise program will include isometric and isotonic regimes to maintain circulatory response reflexes and muscle tone. Any vigorous, jumping type of exercise is out of the question for even a sneeze could propel the astronaut across the cabin. There are plans to provide some of the benefits of exercise through electrical vibrators.

Protection against heat and cold is not as problematical as protection against radiation. There are several sources of heat—including the sun—and, unfortunately, several sources of radiation. One is the ionizing radiation from the electrons already injected into geomagnetic fields by high-altitude nuclear detonation. While the atmosphere protects us from most forms of radiation on earth, a special shield will be required to protect the man in space; some drugs have been developed to safeguard the astronaut's body cells against radiation damage.

Finally, there are psychological problems to consider. The crew members selected will, obviously, be men who are adaptable and who work well under the stress and strain of restricted living and monotonous routine. Recreation schedules will have to be arranged to maintain a high level of motivation. Fortunately, TV programs can be transmitted from the earth, communications will be open, allowing monitoring and early correction of stress-provoking situations.

Important psychological information has already been gathered from submarine missions and in remote Antarctic outposts: the effects of confinement; cabin atmosphere and toxicants; work-rest cycles; personality conflicts. Group behavior and the effects of closed-life support systems have been examined in simulated space vehicle cabins for periods up to 30 days. No doubt, much of the psychological findings of space travel will be applicable to the ever-increasing crowded environments found on earth—in our cities, offices, and homes.

Engineers and scientists have been developing numerous devices and techniques for astronaut comfort and survival during prolonged space travel. In addition to the constant demands of bodily needs and the routine tasks of running the space craft, researchers have also been considering the astronaut's mental needs. These needs are not constant. Instead they appear to pass through various stages: (1) a period of heightened anxiety during the launch and early preparation of the space craft after launching; (2) relatively mild depression—interrupted by some moments of elation—as the astronaut marks time during his long journey; (3) suppressed hostility comes to the surface, near the end of the trip and routine "housekeeping" is neglected; (4) the emotional level is heightened in anticipation of the return to normal living.

Most of the mental needs, peculiar to each phase of space travel, can be satisfied by verbal and visual communication with others outside of the spacecraft.

It was found that of all the apparatus required for space travel, the items that are considered safely "nailed down" are the communications and navigation equipment. In this area, little challenge to existing technology is anticipated, even for the next decade.

Comfortable operating conditions—the so-called shirt-sleeve environment—requires a normal cabin temperature range of 72°-95° F. Ideally, a temperature range between 74°-78° F with a 50 per cent average humidity is a desired goal. To assist the astronaut in moving from one part of the space craft to another, he will be provided with hand holds, guide poles and ropes plus adhesive, magnetized or suction-type footgear. Of course, the astronaut can "soar" from one place to another, but this is not easy. In soaring, the major problem is to maintain body control after push-off and to avoid smashing into an opposite wall. Self-propulsion by using a "reaction gun"—something like a carbon dioxide fire extinguisher—has been tried by astronauts in "space walks." But it is difficult to avoid thrust misalignment with the astronaut's center of mass, which causes random tumbling. Of course, there is also the problem of applying a retroforce at the destination to avoid crashing into a surface and bouncing back.

There are hundreds of daily activities taken for granted on the ground, but which becomes problematical in space. For example, shaving and brushing one's teeth. To remove beard growth, an instrument similar to an electric shaver will be used. But because the fuel to provide electrical power will be as carefully rationed as oxygen, water, and food, the device will have a coil spring that must be hand-wound. (This will provide exercise for the astronaut.) The whisker fuzz will be drawn in by brushes and vacuumed into the razor.

Brushing teeth in the conventional manner is unthinkable. Spitting would be hazardous because the entire inner surfaces of the cabin would be coated with the spray. The astronauts' "brushing" is accomplished by swishing a foaming dentifrice in the mouth, which, being "fortified" with nutrients, can then be swallowed.

For such reasons as making emergency repairs, the astronaut will have to leave the space craft and venture into the void of space. While he can clamber to the outside of the craft in a close-fitting space suit and move about under his own power, it would not be done just to prove it can be done. When the astronaut is to perform some useful task that requires a relatively long period of time, such as repairing a meteorite puncture in the space craft, he will need most of the individual equipment that is provided for him inside; with the possible exception of a food supply and body waste disposal. Among such needs are a thermal control system, radiation and micrometeorite protection, a supply of oxygen, a carbon dioxide regenerator, a communication system, and some sort of navigational equipment to maintain his orientation. Additionally, he needs flood-lights for work on the space craft's dark side, and some sort of automatic polarizing system to protect him from the direct glare on the sun's side. All of these accessories would have to be powered by a self-contained electric energy source. An alternate mode is available by means of an umbilical connection to the space craft for the various power and life-support systems he would be carrying with him, as is done in the current Gemini program.

Then there is the problem of tools. Conceive of an astronaut trying to remove a bolt with a wrench in a conventional manner. He would probably spin around while the nut remained stationary. This problem is solved by providing anchor fittings for hand and foot holds as well as an adjustable strap or protruding arm which is anchored in a convenient place to absorb the reaction forces. Most likely, a complete set of tools will be designed precisely for this type of application. Chance Vought Astronautics division has developed a hand tool called a "plench." This combination pliers and wrench is a squeeze action ratchet tool which can drive socket wrenches or screwdriver bits. A pin protruding from the face of the tool parallel to the axis of rotation fits into a socket next to the bolt or screw hole to absorb the torque reaction.

For reasons of safety and maneuverability the astronaut will have to communicate with others inside the space craft. Typical of the communication devices being developed is a radio transmitter-receiver designed to be tucked away in a human ear. Although it is located in the ear, it is still sensitive enough to pick up the wearer's voice signals, and then transmit the sounds for short distances. This small ear microphone is being developed by Space Labs, Incorporated, for the National Aeronautics and Space Administration. It provides continuous communications over long periods of time without discomfort.

Voice signals originating in the space craft are sent as radio waves and picked up by the receiver in the ear microphone much like a home radio receiver. Conversely, sounds spoken by the wearer of the ear microphone are picked up after they have passed to his outer ear through his head (partially through his Eustachian tube and partially through the jaw and skull bones) rather than by conduction through the air from his mouth to the ear. Power for this radio transmitter-receiver is provided by a small battery which surprisingly is also inserted into the wholly ear-contained device. Imagine the potential uses for such a device in more conventional applications. It is the next best thing to mental telepathy.

A number of measures will have to be taken to counter the harmful and deteriorative effects of space travel on the body. For example, it is known that gravity plays an important part in the cardiovascular system to provide proper blood circulation. That is, the heart does not accomplish all blood circulation by itself. Muscular movement, as in walking, "squeezes" much of the blood to its proper destination. (This is why we stretch upon awakening.)

To provide this squeezing action, pressure cuffs are built into the arms or legs of space suits or can be attached periodically to the astronaut in his "shirt-sleeve" environment. The cuffs automatically inflate and deflate rhythmically, thus artificially providing blood movement and preventing cardiovascular deterioration. Controlled breathing exercises will help keep the respiratory system functioning properly and special exercises will keep the endocrine system in reasonable working order. Isometric tension exercises will help the cardiovascular, respiratory, muscular, skeletal, gastro-intestinal, and endocrine systems. And, as previously mentioned, centrifuging will be beneficial to virtually all systems.

An important part of space travel is the continuous or periodic measuring of body and mental conditions in order to keep the astronaut in good condition. Measurements will include blood pressure, pulse and respiration rate and volume, blood and urine sampling, body temperature and body mass (weight), muscle size and strength. Electrocardiograms and electroencephalographs are desirable, but it is not known whether such cumbersome equipment is feasible. However, these devices can be miniaturized; strap-on heartbeat meters no larger than a dime plus blood pressure measuring devices that can be worn on a finger like a ring and skin temperature measuring devices have already been developed. There will also be psychological and behavioral tests to establish the mental state of the astronauts. This information will be fed into a computer which, in turn, provides warning signals when something goes wrong. The information would also be telemetered back to earth for analysis. In addition, a possible weekly medical examination would be administered by the crew physician. These monitoring chores are expected to make up the bulk of an astronaut's daily work load.

While every possible means will be taken to provide for the crew's safety and well being, there are many unknowns which will have to await actual experiences. For example, the combined effects of extended weightlessness, boredom, and contaminated atmospheres is something that cannot be duplicated by any earth experiment. Developing the means to counteract the harmful influences of these conditions is the purpose of the Air Force's Manned Orbiting Laboratory (MOL). Also, much more will have to be known about individual differences; why some people suffer from motion sickness while others do not and why people react differently in an emergency.

As has happened since time immemorial, the answer to one problem has generated a new problem to be answered. However, it is significant to note that man has never yet reached a barrier that he has not found some way to break through. The barriers of space will prove no different.

It is evident we are in a transitional situation that brings many conflicts. Each new development brought about by man's flight from the bounds of earth tends to substantiate the mechanistic theory that everything about man can be explained in mechanical (or chemical or physical) terms. Yet our culture, religions, tradition, and in some part our medical practice, as we have seen, are based on man being considered as more than a machine. Whatever the "true" nature of man, our increasingly mechanistic environment calls for an increasing mechanistic treatment of man. As we become more dependent on machines, we ourselves have to think and act more like machines: similar to natives of a conquered nation having to learn the language and customs and abide by the legal system of the more powerful nation. In fact, man is becoming so dependent on the machine that in certain situations—the space exploration for one—the question arises that perhaps the machine could perform its tasks better without the encumbrance of man.

Many prominent people—scientists and engineers included—question the worth of sending an astronaut into space at all. There are, they claim, too many unsolved problems on the ground which require the time, effort, and money being spent on space projects. Is not the elimination of poverty, ignorance, and sickness a more worthy pursuit?

But other equally prominent people feel that the great value of space exploration justifies the time and expense, but question the desirability, or even the need, of sending a man. Why not let the machines (implying that they can do a better job than man) perform all the tasks? For the purpose of this book we will not analyze the value of space travel per se. Instead we will examine the pros and cons of three alternatives: man-controlled spacecraft, man and machine controlled, and machine alone controlled.

The human controller or operator can adapt himself to a wide variety of situations and he can learn. While machines can adapt, learn and even be self-motivated, as we will see in subsequent chapters, man is better able "to get the job done" at present. Man's adaptive skill is illustrated by his ability to ride a bicycle, drive a car, or control a spacecraft. He can also collect, assimilate, and act on many different kinds of information from the outside world; from the things he sees, the sounds he hears, from instrument dials and "from the seat of his pants." Man can be highly selective of the information presented. He can filter out superfluous or unneeded information and "dig deeper" to find information he needs that is not readily available. While we do not know exactly how, man can learn to do many things. The term "learn" is being used in its broadest sense. For example, a five-year-old can be taught to ride a two-wheel bicycle. This feat represents a myriad of functions— sensing, balancing, controlling, and integrating functions. Yet the five-year-old can do all of these things without knowing the meaning of any one of them. Mature men such as astronauts can do equally well with more complicated tasks, like controlling a space vehicle.

The extent of human capability at adapting was brought vividly home to me in an experience during Morse Code training in the Army. I had difficulty attaining a ten-word-per-minute code receiving level, which was the minimum requirement. The "student" next to me was a commercial telegraph operator. The fact that he could receive, translate, and type 120 words per minute was not as amazing as the fact that he could hold a conversation with me at the same time.

Among other reasons for using men rather than a machine are found in man's flexibility in handling varying modes of operation, sequences of events, and emergencies; his originality in creating new patterns or meaningful combinations of established patterns; his cleverness and versatile knowledge; and his resourcefulness in overcoming unexpected obstacles.

It is, however, highly visionary to expect man to control every aspect of space travel or lunar exploration without the aid of machines and instrumentation. Man can perhaps be most productive when his talents are combined with the capabilities of mechanisms. For example, man has little trouble navigating aircraft, but he needs power boosts to move the various control surfaces. Or in high speed flight, he needs automatic stabilizing augmentation. By combining man and machines, the strong points of one complement the weak points of the other.

It is flattering to think that man can deal with most situations alone. It is also comforting to know that machines can perform those tasks man is ill-equipped or not equipped to do. But technological advance seems to sweep man to one side as it surges forward. As our space vehicles, for instance, become more complex, the need for more control and operative functions that are beyond man's ability to provide increases. With the development of fully automated systems, the question is raised as to whether we can afford to have the astronaut (who has to be fed, kept warm, provided with air, etc.) go along on a space trip or perform lunar or planetary explorations. To many technical people, the astronaut is as welcome on these trips as a mother-in-law on a honeymoon. The arguments these engineers and scientists present are ego-deflating, but they are thought provoking.

While man is adaptive and can learn, these abilities cannot be taken for granted in every situation. Unique and marvelous as man is, he is extremely complicated; it is often difficult to "fit" him into the system, and his performance under severe environmental stress is not known. He can assimilate many bits of information, but only when he can focus attention on them one at a time. He is superior in selecting and sensing energy inputs with his eyes, ears, and body. Nevertheless the scientists are not quite sure how this multifaceted system works and, consequently, how best to use it. While motivation is wonderful and as yet has not been designed into a machine, it is extremely difficult to control and understand. For example, when the astronaut is suffering from fatigue, fear, anger, and jealousy, he is difficult to "motivate." A situation or condition

that would be unacceptable to him when in a high state of motivation may be overlooked or rationalized away if he becomes indiffer-
ent to it.

While there is variability among machines, it is insignificant in
comparison to the variability of people. Each man learns, adapts,
reacts, operates, and generally behaves differently. It cannot be
taken for granted that two men will react in the same manner to
a given situation. Furthermore, the complexity of man makes predicting his reaction to a hypothetical situation, likely to occur on
a space trip, exceedingly difficult. Those advocating complete removal of man from the space vehicle argue further that man is
error-prone, relatively weak and tires quickly, is easily confused,
influenced by temperament and by distractions, misunderstands
and is misunderstood, seldom gets along with others in an isolated
group, and on and on.

Despite the downgrading of man's ability, few deny that man is
useful when something goes wrong with the machine. This has
been proved in the orbital flights already made. Concepts and
theory about what man can and cannot do remain in a state of
flux. Calm and reasonable thinkers do not argue on a man *versus*
machine basis. Engineers and industrial designers realize their
time is most profitably spent learning how to design machines
which bring out the best—and not the worst—in man. Psychologists,
physiologists, and physicians are determined to understand man
and how he operates (the findings are both intriguing and pleasant). Together these specialists are creating a man *and* machine
combination that literally can conquer new worlds.

How to fathom the deeper meaning in the human and/or machine control of a space vehicle? Obviously, a space vehicle is
simply an example—albeit a shiny one—of broader and more in-
clusive transference of human functions to machines. Considered
in its entirety, is the man-machine relationship merely a case of
human masters finding quiet, efficient mechanical slaves to do their
bidding? Or possibly, was Thoreau right when he said, "Man is
becoming the tool of his tools."

We cannot ignore the significance in the trend toward a relative
strengthening of machines and the relegation of man to a lesser
and lesser position, even if only by comparison. Many have noted

the trend and have felt compelled to speak out. Their warnings are usually variations on the theme: "Turn back you fools! Turn back before it is too late!" In all of the fictional stories at least, when warnings were given (by the prophetic character who either had been "there" or knew what to expect "there"), the warnings went unheeded. There obviously would be no story if those warned did or could turn back.

If an astronaut, and the country that sponsors his trip, wishes to explore the moon or Mars, dependence must be placed to an even greater degree on machinery. The old slogan must become "Leave the driving *and the thinking* to us—the "us" refers to the automatic pilot, the automatic safety devices, the automatic computer, and so on. However, if man places himself physically and mentally in the care of the machine, he may find on his return to earth that he is ill equipped to face the primitive realities of life, because, figuratively and literally, he has excreted his backbone.

For the sake of any astronauts who may read the above paragraph, I hasten to point out that no detraction of ability or courage is intended. Very few of us who confine our existence to the protectiveness of earth have the strength, and especially the nerve, to attempt the perilous journey. What is intended is an allegorical picture of the present state of civilization: a picture characterized by the wish to go faster and farther; the quest for greater knowledge; the desire for an easier life; and the hope for more security. But as folk tales and literature suggest, we may get our wishes but will be totally unprepared to pay the consequences once they are granted.

Our predicament is not whether to let the Genie out of his jar; we have already done that. It is not how to get him back in; we cannot do that. Our problem is how to get along with all of the "gifts" we have asked for and which the technological Genie has granted us. In a nutshell, we cannot run away from our machine dominated world any more than ancient man could escape from the biosphere. But we can change the dybosphere somewhat to serve our best interests, and change ourselves somewhat to adapt to it. If the cave man had not done this with his environment and himself, we would not be here today to discuss today's problems.

In any event, we can see that the mechanization of man creates a conflict. The conflict is especially strong in those who do not subscribe to a 100 per cent mechanistic theory: those who say there is more to man than can be explained in physical terms. Both the mechanists and the vitalists can see man being carried relentlessly into the dybosphere along the tracks his technological thinking has laid out. But the vitalists say the speed and the singleness in direction of man's journey blocks his insight into spiritual wisdom which cannot be put in technological terms. The loss of this spiritual wisdom is unfortunate, they claim, because the deprivation comes at a time when man is at the peak of his tug of war with mechanical devices, the struggle being over whether man is to drive or merely be driven. The mechanists on the other hand would prefer that we had a roadmap with which to follow the journey, but that such a roadmap is not essential because whether we drive or are driven, the destination, they feel, is essentially the same.

Let me cite a simple example to underline the point. In Olympic games of antiquity, the high jump was performed by man without any aids. Then the pole vault was added in which man could reach higher levels by means of a hand held pole that serves as a kind of lever. With the rigid pole a contestant could reach a height of about fourteen feet. So far there is no complaint. But more recently the pole, instead of being essentially rigid as with bamboo or aluminum, was made of flexible Fiberglas. The champion now can vault about seventeen feet. The point, as made by many dissenters, is that the contestant drives himself fourteen feet *and is driven* the extra three feet by the mechanics of the vaulting arrangement and not by his strength. The dissenters feel such a contest is equivalent to getting to the top of Mt. Everest by helicopter.

Broadly, there are those who say that man's objective is to go as high as possible (the moon? Mars? Pluto?). They feel that mechanical aid is not only desirable, but necessary. Then there are those who say that man should go only as high as his own strength allows—moral strength included. This latter group feels that mechanical aid is not only undesirable, but unnecessary. But who is right?

The laws of nature apply to man as much as they do to the rest of the universe. The natural forces that drive and govern celestial bodies also drive and govern human bodies. The motion of the earth is constant and this constancy of motion is repeated in man; the earth does not stand still, nor does man. The force that spins the earth on its axis is related to the force that makes man seek higher and higher levels. And he strives for these levels in the most efficient way possible. While some say this striving is wrong, others say it is for the best. The striving (we call it the search for progress) is unalterably regulated by the same mechanical forces that generate it. Put in simple terms, man is continually under pressure to change as is everything else.

Evolution brings change, and man is capable of changing himself to a greater degree than any other species. Ancient man "changed himself" by putting on clothing for protection against the glacial frosts. Perhaps anything man does in the future, by comparison, will not be any more significant; but it will be more drastic.

From prehistoric times, man has been "modifying" himself for decorative, hygienic, or religious reasons. More recently, vestigial or rudimentary organs such as adenoids, tonsils, and the appendices are removed almost as a matter of course. Most recently, there have been operations such as labiotomies, vaginotomies, and gastrotomies in which major body parts are severed, destroyed, or cut out to alleviate some otherwise incurable condition. It is simple to predict that the future course of body modification will range from the corrective, to the preventive, to the improving.

Corrective operations will be performed to strengthen certain "design weaknesses" of the body. For example, the reverse bend at the base of the spine—caused when man adopted an erect position —is the source of much back trouble. There is no reason to believe the biomechanical engineers can not design a more structurally sound spinal column. Preventive operations will be performed to allow the body to withstand greater stresses. For example, plastic skull caps can be installed under the scalp or steel rods can be put in leg and arm bones to reinforce them. However, it is the area of "improvement" operations that causes the mind to reel (and maybe the stomach to turn queazy).

As a starter, it is known that certain individuals and races are better than others at withstanding pain, extreme cold and heat, or at surviving for long periods without food, water, or even buried in the ground. No doubt these Eskimos, Bedouins, Tibetans and Yogins have physical and mental characteristics which can be duplicated in others. Dr. Toby Freedman of North American Aviation, Inc. starts with these concepts and then goes further to develop what he calls an Optiman—"a man whose outward appearance is quite normal, but who has been adapted to the oxygen requirements of a Himalayan Sherpa, the heat resistance of a walker-on-coals, who needs less food than a hermit, who has the strength of a wrestler, and who runs a mile in three minutes while solving problems of tensor analysis in his head."

Beyond the Optiman concept is the Cyborg of Dr. Nathan Kline and Manfred Clynes at the Rockland State Hospital in Orangeburg, New York. The Cyborg (short for cybernetic organism) would be a human being—allegedly—modified most radically. The Cyborg is an example of extreme alteration of the human body to better adapt it to new or changing environments and would be able to travel in an unsealed cabin through the vacuum of space as well as walk on the surface of the moon or Mars without the conventional space suit of current-day astronauts. To a large degree, the Cyborg is a continuation of the trend of "building-in" artificial aids as opposed to merely hanging them on as in the case of eyeglasses and externally worn hearing aids.

The Cyborg would be encased in a skintight suit. There would be no need for pressurization as his lungs would be partially collapsed and the temperature of the blood lowered. Respiration and most of the other body functions would be performed for him dybologically. In other words, the body processes such as breathing, eating, and waste removal would be computer controlled in the same manner as the chemical processes of a petroleum plant are now. His metabolism would be kept in a constant state regardless of wide external temperature or pressure changes. Communication would be accomplished through the use of an ear-microphone-transmitter-receiver device similar to the one previously described.

Essentially, the Cyborg represents one further step in the "compression" of a closed ecological system. Normally, the environment on earth (its atmosphere, plants, animals, water, etc.) is man's first "home." Later, houses were built which provided some of the more desirable aspects of the "natural" environment and excluded most of the undesirable ones. Then man completely duplicated this "home" within the confines of a space vehicle. Finally, the thinking is to package the "home" as completely within the human body as possible and to put what is left over in cannisters to be carried on, and internally connected to, the back of the body.

Thus, in this part of the book we have seen that man is becoming more mechanized in almost every sense of the word. In the next part, we shall examine and discuss the topic parallel to the mechanization of humans; the humanization of machines.

PART III
HUMANIZING
MACHINES

Chapter Six

The Machine Today

The machine unmasks the man.
Now that machines are so perfect,
the engineer is nobody.

— *Emerson*

Man marches into the dybosphere with a companion. One that in the strict biological sense is not even "alive." The companion is the machine: The machine that used to clink and clank, that now hums and buzzes, and that soon will operate with the same noiseless efficiency that man does. (Ironically, man will start to hum and buzz as he is fitted with artificial organs, and then clink and clank as he is fitted with artificial limbs. No doubt acoustical engineers, who design silent running submarines, will be called upon to quiet down the electrical and mechanical gear installed in people.)

As the machine progresses it will resemble man more and more, both physically and mentally. To this end, the machine is becoming humanized.

In the preceding part of the book we examined the mechanizing process of man in detail. In this part we will examine the humanizing process of the machine in detail.

You may ask why the parallel between man and machine is drawn as tightly as it is. The answer is simply that the unvarying laws of nature act as consistently for machines as they do for man. The confusion is due to the general notion that if man did not build machines they would not exist. To a considerable degree this is true, for in the scheme of things man came first. If machines had entered the scene first, there is no reason—theoretically at least—why machines could not have "built" people.

Those who agree with Darwin that man developed by an evolutionary process would as readily agree that machines developed by an innovationary process. Yet, many have a tendency to mentally construct separate logic-tight compartments in which evolution and innovation are not allowed to be considered together—let alone to be equated. Perhaps a detailed look at the machines of the present and those anticipated for the future will allow the reader to judge for himself the degree to which machines and man are becoming more and more similar.

It should be emphasized that the machines which will be described either exist or their operational feasibility has been firmly established in research models. This is not science fiction.

At the start of the book we traced the crude and uncertain beginnings of hand tools, wind and water driven power generating mills, and machine tools. From these beginnings new machines have been—and are being—developed through a close cooperation of technology and biology, within which the laws of life are applied to mechanics.

Machines have grown in number and complexity. Their growth has evoked wonder which is justified, and fear which is not. The fear stems from an unfamiliarity of the inner workings of a device. You might remember the trepidation and almost unaccountable feeling of horror that people felt when they first used the telephone or heard a voice from an early radio.

The clock is another interesting example. There has always been an intellectual and philosophical fascination with time. The concept of time is profound because it is not a "thing" which can be seen or felt. Time was revered because man was aware of it only through his inner being. When someone invented a means to measure and to display time, the beautiful illusion was shattered. The contrivance which could make time real and which could act and move on its own without life of its own was viewed with a mixture of awe and resentment. The people who observed those early clocks saw mostly in the springs, escapement, and in the gears, a device which personified the relentless movement toward old age and death. They saw a lifeless, but life-like, device that intruded itself into the very cells of the body and which evoked a feeling a coldness and impending doom. Movie directors even today use a ticking clock to evoke a mood of suspense and the foreboding of evil deeds or situations.

But as one who has taken apart and examined many clocks I do not find anything inherent in the mechanisms to justify any feeling other than respect for the craftsmanship of manufacturer and a deep sense of admiration for the inventor. In the same way, if recent and future technological advances in machines are understood, fear is not necessary.

The speed of our race into the dybosphere is brought to our attention most sharply when considering the basic building blocks of electronic equipment. Robot-like devices, computers, machines that see and learn, and equipment that essentially can replace the design engineer are dramatic—as we will see shortly. But these developments are not as profound and hardly as rapid as are the changes taking place in electronic circuitry, or "packaging" as it is sometimes called. The size, weight, failure rate, power consumption, and cost of an individual circuit such as a radio amplifier stage or a computer on-off logic device were cut in half almost every year from World War II to 1960. Since 1960, this amount of improvement has occurred about every six months.

It is this rate of improvement that allows the building of faster airplanes, more sophisticated space vehicles, and near instantaneous communication systems. To be practical, there must be an inverse relationship between the complexity of a product and the characteristics of its constituent parts. As an example, the number of electronic component parts carried aboard bomber aircraft in its avionic equipment (radars, navigators, autopilots, communications, computers, etc.) about doubles every five years. If there was not such improvement in component size, cost, weight and so forth, the bombers would be too large and heavy to get off the ground.

Perhaps increasing even faster than the intricacies of electronic components is the terminology used to describe them. Engineers and scientists generally use every conceivable device in the semantic bag of tricks to name the things they discover or develop. If a certain atomic particle looks as big as a barn compared to other particles, the physicists use it as a new unit of measure called, logically, a barn; just as a radar with two round ear-like antennas is called a

Mickey-Mouse radar. Radar itself is an acronym (from radio detection and ranging).

Engineers also like euphonious—and meaningful—abbreviations, and generate them by the thousands. For example, there is SNAP (space nuclear auxiliary power) and SAD SAM (Sentence Appraiser and Diagrammer-Semantic Machine). New words are coined (incidentally, COIN means counter insurgency to the aeronautical engineer) such as NOR for neither-or, and NAND for neither-and. This semi-apology for the fertility of the technologists' word generating ability is made only so the reader will know I am serious when I speak of a "set-reset trigger flip-flop single chip integrated circuit." The reader will also understand how convenient it is for the engineer to refer to this simply as an *SFF* circuit.

In the early days of radio, life was more simple. The transmitting tubes were—and still are—called "bottles" because that is what they resemble. Other electronic tubes were called acorn tubes, lighthouse tubes and the like, also because of their shape. But as these vacuum tubes became smaller they were called miniature tubes, and then, as they became even smaller, subminiature tubes. Around this time (the mid-1950's), transistors appeared. Electronic circuitry was fashioned from individual components—resistors, capacitors, tubes or transistors, and so on, wired to terminal strips or to each other. This type of electronic packaging was called discrete circuitry. Then, to conserve space, these discrete components were stacked together like cordwood and encapsulated into a plastic block. Logically, these blocks, or modules, were called cordwood circuits.

Around 1958 new fabrication techniques were developed out of necessity. Simply making components smaller and squeezing them closer together reached the point of diminishing returns. Electronics manufacturing was turning into a jeweler's art. Rather than adapting former design approaches, microminiaturization techniques were developed. In microminiaturization (one step beyond the subminiaturization mentioned earlier) circuits were made by electrochemical processes. In this way, transistors, resistors, capacitors, coils and such were deposited on 0.3-inch-square ceramic plates. For example, complete circuits such as a flip-flop circuit were fabricated under a microscope. This particular circuit contained about sixteen individual components, including two transistors, and was packaged in a volume hardly larger than a single conventional transistor of that time. Circuits packaged in this way were called micromodules. The micromodules, in turn, were fashioned like a tinker-toy set to form a complete unit. Needless to say, larger versions of these micromodules had already been called tinker-toy circuits. At this stage of development, a complete radio receiver could be squeezed into a fountain pen size container.

A year later (which in the field of electronics can represent a whole generation) microminiaturization was replaced by molecular electronics or molectronics, in its shortened form. In typical governmentese language, the Air Force defined molectronics "as the synthesis of matter with predetermined electronic properties so that under a particular stimuli, the matter exhibits complex and complete electronic functions that previously were performed by distinctive combinations of active and passive components."

The engineers quickly christened this type of electronic item a "functional electronic block," or FEB and called them "Feebs" for short. A FEB, for example, could be a 100 microwatt band-pass amplifier. The molectronic approach depended heavily on gathering basic information locked within the atoms, molecules and crystals of matter.

In 1960, a complete digital guidance computer was made by the Radio Corporation of America for the Army. The 260 micromodules in this four-pound computer were mounted in egg-crate-type frames and then soldered to a printed-circuit backplate, called the mother-board. Individual micromodules, about one-half inch square, could be removed quite easily from the frame in case of failure.

Continuing the trend toward smaller, more reliable, less costly electronic circuits, the early 1960's brought microelectronics. The technology of microelectronics is generally referred to as integrated-circuitry. This is because the various elements of the circuit is a monolithic whole rather than a group of discrete parts connected by wires. The integrated-circuit technology uses two different approaches. One is the thin-film process in which passive components such as resistors and capacitors and interconnections are deposited in layers (as many as thirteen or more) on a chip of inert material or substrate. The other is the semiconductor diffusion process, in which active and passive elements are formed within a tiny chip of a semiconductor material, usually silicon. The thin-film technology uses evaporation, sputtering, or vacuum deposition to lay down passive components on an insulator or dielectric material. Active elements, such as transistors or diodes are attached to thin-film circuits by bonded, welded, or soldered connections. The semiconductor technology uses complex manufacturing processes such as patterned metal-film alloying to make both active and passive elements within a single chip or block of semiconductor material.

The two types of microcircuitry have their own advantages and disadvantages. Current cost of each type is about $10-$16. Because thin-film circuits are ideal for passive components and semiconductor integrated circuits (called SICs) are ideal for active components, a hybrid technology has been developed. The hybrid types —essentially a combination of the two earlier technologies—have worked well in a number of systems already. To many engineers active in the field, they represent the direction in which the technology must evolve. It is estimated that the integrated circuit market will reach $1.2 billion by 1970.

This dollar volume is hard to reconcile with the optimistic cost reductions predicted for integrated microcircuitry. Currently, about four hundred circuits are made on a single silicon wafer and then sliced off like pieces of fudge. Each circuit is about 30-50 thousandths of an inch square (about 6-10 human hairs wide) and may contain a two-phase shift register made up of 33 transistors, 27 resistors and two diodes. The cost of fabricating such circuits is estimated at less than ten cents. A flip-flop circuit containing 14 transistors, 10 resistors and two capacitors is estimated to cost less than two cents. Of course, the circuits require connection leads and encapsulation; but with mechanical handling and packaging the cost is not substantially increased. Currently under development is a single monolithic chip containing 16 circuits for a total of 148 electronic elements. This complexity (which includes 80 transistors) approaches that of a TV receiver. Already available is a single-chip microcircuit (a 90-bit shift register, 58- by 80-thousandths of an inch in size) which contains, among other components, 550 transistors.

With thin-film techniques, discrete details of one-millionth of an inch are possible. Using such techniques, it is possible to put the entire Bible—and five foreign translations of it—on the head of a pin.

While this degree of complexity is not as great as that found in a living cell, it approaches it. On the other hand, the speed of communication in electronic components is a million times faster than in biological organisms.

Microminiaturization represents a profound engineering development in itself. But the significance of this development has effects that reach far beyond simple diminution in size. When documents were hand-lettered by scribes, there was a one-to-one relationship between cost and the number of words on a page. With the advent of mechanical printing, the cost per page varied little as a function of the number of words. The same is true with electronic equipment. When individual components are hand-inserted and hand-wired, the cost is directly proportional to complexity. Because of this there is great pressure to reduce the number of parts in conventionally produced equipment such as a radio or TV even at the expense of performance and reliability. With microelectronic circuits (which essentially are produced by a printing process) increased complexity adds little to the cost. Consequently, equipment using these new devices can make use of additional complexity to enhance performance and reliability at lower than ever cost. For example, with little added expense a computer using microelectronic circuits can have built-in redundancy to increase its useful life and can provide self-checking circuits to signal an incipient failure. Also, extra-performance features can be provided which hitherto had been prohibitively expensive.

Pursuing the example further, we find in the use of microelectronic circuits another instance of the growth of machines and the decline (relatively speaking) of man. Due to the high cost of building computers using conventional components and assembly methods, it was more economical to have the human programmer spoon-feed predigested information into the computer in the form of codes. Now the tables are turned. In relation to the cost of human programmers, it is now more economically feasible to have instructions fed into the computer in plain English and, by making the computer more complex, have the computer do the necessary coding.

Put simply, the trend is for the machine to do more brain work and the human to do less.

Now we move from the "subcellular" level of a dybological machine to the complete "body" level. Mechanical man was predestined to be called a robot ever since Karel Capek wrote his play about Rossum's Universal Robots which, like engineers, he put in the initialized form R.U.R. (Incidentally, robot means serf or peasant in the Czech language.) A robot is the dybological equivalent of the biological man. But it is interesting to note that a person who acts or works mechanically and without thinking for himself is called a robot. This again indicates how hopeless a task it is to keep human terms and machine terms exclusively distinct; they are bound to be applied interchangeably.

Robots are built essentially for two reasons: (1) to duplicate and thus study some characteristic of man; (2) to perform useful acts in their own right. The first type of robot looks or acts like a man because of its purpose. The second may resemble man in some ways but the similarity is not deliberate. Instead it is because the functional aspects of the work to be performed are related.

Typical of the first type of robots are the synthetic men that serve as stand-ins for dangerous experiments. For example, they may be parachuted from a plane, tested in ejection seats, whirled in centrifuges, and crashed in an automobile. These robots are instrumented to feel heat and cold, to sense shock in a way that is equivalent to pain, and even to breathe. They are anthropomorphic in that they have the shape of men, and are anthropometric in that they weigh the same as man, and have the same center of gravity. They can be made to talk and walk like men when the need arises. The "insides" of these robots contain strain gages, accelerometers, and telemetering transmitters which measure and relay almost-human reactions when, for instance, they are ejected from a sled traveling at 1500 miles per hour.

A mannequin with quite human-like "insides" is a life-size model patient developed by the University of Southern California School of Medicine. This work was done in conjunction with the Aerojet-General Corporation's Van Karman Center under a grant from the Department of Health, Education and Welfare. This life-like, computer controlled mannequin was developed to speed and improve the training of young physicians learning to be anesthesiologists. Student doctors can practice on the mannequin without fearing the consequences of a mistake. The mannequin simulates breathing, heart beat and pulse, opens and closes its eyes, dilates its pupils, opens its mouth, and extends its tongue. It also wrinkles its eyebrows, tenses and relaxes its vocal cords, coughs, twitches its shoulder muscles, vomits, and also can change color from pink to blue to ashen gray.

The mannequin's most important function is to help anesthesiology students learn to insert an airway tube down a patient's throat for artificial lung ventilation—a common practice, but one requiring skill and speed. Added advantages include the ability to simulate emergency situations such as a massive heart attack to test student physicians' reaction in moments of crisis, as well as to help in the training of proper administration of drugs, the proper use of oxygen face masks and other anesthesiological techniques. When the mannequin, being built by the Sierra Engineering Company, is completed, it will be sensitive to varying dosages of ten different drugs.

There has been a rather amazing type of robot already built of the second type. This is a mobile automaton with complex behavioral patterns so that it can "exist" in varied environments. The scientists at the Johns Hopkins University Applied Physics Laboratory developed what they affectionately call "The Beast" (a name given it by the newsmen who wanted something with more appeal than an "adaptive mobile automaton"). Shaped like a king-sized hat box with a retractable giraffe-like head, the device "thinks" for itself. It also "eats" when hungry, "plays" when it feels good, "sleeps" when tired, and "panics" when it gets into trouble. When its tiny sensors, which follow along a wall's surface, "feel" for one of four available outlets, the machine's head positions itself and two prongs lock into the socket. The robot feeds itself until its batteries are fully recharged and then wanders aimlessly in a playful mood until it is time to eat once more. It can survive on its own for almost a day in the halls. During this period it plugs into the electrical outlets about 25 times.

The ability to avoid obstacles such as a tangle of electrical cables or bumping into people has been stored in the device's electronic logic element. When The Beast approaches a stairway, it shudders and backs away. This reaction comes from eight little white "shoes" around its circumference, which indicate holes in the floor or absence of support. Should the machine get tangled-up in a railing, for instance, with its head caught between two poles, it wiggles its head back and forth in a human-like fashion. Then it completely stops and goes into a "panic" mode before trying another maneuver to get free.

Then there are space robots, called "telepuppets" developed by Dr. Whipple of the Smithsonian Institute's Astrophysical Observatory. These are remote-controlled devices which will repair each other as well as their equipment and serve as crew members of vehicles exploring space. The space robots will be supervised and guided from earth by television.

The General Electric Company has developed a robot-type machine called "Handyman" for remote-control work with radioactive materials. The Handyman "hears," "feels," and to a very limited degree "thinks" for itself. It can lift weights as well as perform delicate tasks such as picking petals off a daisy. The Handyman essentially consists of a pair of mechanical arms and hands in roughly human form which are connected electrically to a harness worn by the operator. By means of this harness and other devices the system causes the mechanical limbs to mimic the actions of a man's arms and hands, while the operator receives signals from the machine conveying information about force and position.

General Electric Project Engineer Ralph Moser reports that the contact between man and machine is so direct and detailed that the operator does not have to think about the mechanics of directing the machine. He simply concentrates on the manipulation task itself, and observes the actions of the mechanical arms and hands as if they were his own. Handyman is designed to be free of any internal forces such as friction, dead weight or the like which would tend to tire the operator or mask the forces he is trying to measure. The amount of force reflected back to the operator is directly proportional to that experienced by the machine.

Care must be taken so that the information sent back is not confusing to the operator. For instance, when the robot's hand grasps a rubber ball, the signal coming back to the operator should tell him whether it is the ball or the fingers that are being compressed. Handyman can perform tasks requiring superhuman strength; can handle microscopic objects; and, when called upon, can operate underwater.

A device similar to Handyman has been developed by General Mills, Incorporated for the Los Alamos Scientific Laboratory. This 25-ton device called the Minotaur, has two arms and three eyes. The Minotaur is mounted on a crane carriage with a rotating platform and was designed to perform maintenance work in a radioactively-contaminated area. The machine's two manipulators provide the same basic motion as the human arms but with somewhat more strength. Each has a reach of three feet. The hand assemblies of Minotaur can be removed by remote control at the wrist joint and can be replaced with impact tools, drills, or other portable electric hand tools. Its three "eyes" are television cameras, two of which are mounted on pivoting booms near the arms for closeup views and the third is placed in a vantage point to provide an overall view of the work area. The radioactively-contaminated equipment to be serviced is located within the forty to fifty foot area which the machine can reach. Control for the system is provided from a desk-type console located in an adjacent room, shielded from any radioactivity. All controls and the three television monitors are installed in the console.

The industrial manipulators just described require all the delicacy of a human operator and represent one specie of robot. There is another type—an industrial robot—which is substituted for an assembler, a machine operator, or a material handler. While the manner in which these robots perform their jobs is human-like, their appearance is more like that of a machine tool. (The public's expectation that a robot should be made in man's image is based more on conceit than on a full understanding of function utility.) These machines perform their work in about the same space taken up by a human. For most manufacturing jobs, these robots have one or more jointed arms with movements equivalent to a human waist, shoulder, elbow, and wrist. While there are machines which perform repetitive tasks without a human operator, they are not classified as robots unless they are equipped with feedback sensors at various joints and with a memory that allows them to perform their tasks without the continuous attendance of a human.

These robots are instructed in the performance of their jobs literally by being "led by the hand." That is, the machine is led through the proper motions for creating an effective work pattern. The various motions are recorded on either magnetic tape or magnetic drums. Examples of the versatility of these machines include: paint spraying of auto parts, operation of forging presses, contour welding of auto frame parts, transfer of parts between punch presses, and spring clip assembly.

These automatic machines now do much routine work, and have thus taken a great deal of the drudgery out of man's labor. They are flexible and can be switched from job to job. In an interesting study, it was found that this type of robot was "sick" only one-third of the time that human workers were. Further, not only can one robot be readily "relieved" by another, but a robot can be replaced by a human worker as well. Another interesting development by users of these robots is the need to keep them fully employed. That is, unless the robot performed tasks on a steady basis, they would not pay for themselves in the allotted time.

There are machines currently being developed which, in themselves, perform a multiplicity of tasks but which, when combined, offer an ability representative of a higher level of complexity. Computer-aided design is an example of this complex functional ability.

Of course computers are already a basic and immeasurable help to the engineer in his design work, the speed of machine calculation makes possible the solving of problems involving many variables and complex computations. But thus far the computer primarily has been used functionally as little more than a slide rule or desk calculator.

To the engineer, creative design is more of a graphic problem than a numerical one. The design process starts with the engineer visualizing a particular configuration, perhaps a truss bridge. Once the general features of the bridge are conceived the engineer faces the menial work of reducing his mental conception to a workable design. This development process consists of selecting structural members, performing stress analyses, and integrating the individual segments into a workable whole. In cases where the engineer is pushing through the frontiers of existing knowledge, he has the additional task of searching out the most recent information in his field or perhaps developing new concepts.

The routine repetitive tasks—the bane of the creative design engineer—are rapidly being turned over to the tireless and uncomplaining computer. These tasks include: design logic (routine decision-making), equation solving and computation (cut-and-dry slide rule work), design checking (to make sure size, weight, cost, and performance are optimized), and paperwork generation (specifications, standardized drawing, wiring diagrams, cost accounting, bill of materials, etc.).

To design a transformer or an electric motor, for instance, requires the selection of a winning combination of, among other things, wire sizes, steel stampings, length-to-width ratios, and cooling arrangements from literally millions of possible combinations. The knowledgeable engineer does not, of course, choose his combinations randomly. He uses his training and intuition to "home-in" on the correct combination. But even with his initial ball-park estimates, the final design results only after a mentally exhausting cut-and-fit process.

The obvious solution for relieving the engineer was to have a general purpose computer duplicate the arts and sciences an engineer uses in his design work. This has been done successfully. And the obvious next step was also taken: having the computer punch out control tapes to electronically direct the work of machine tools along the production line. Essentially, this last step bypasses the traditional drafting board effort. The net result of this mechanization has been to upgrade the engineer. By freeing him from mundane work, he spends more of his time creatively—in new product research, and in determining customer needs.

Yet, because thousands of engineers have been released to do creative work, an information explosion has occurred in the field of technical literature. Again, the computer has been called upon to solve a problem it has inadvertently fostered.

What is the size of the information retrieval problem? Each year the engineers and scientists produce 60,000 books, 100,000 research treatises, and 1.3-million articles. World-wide, these same technical people thumb their way through 55,000 different magazines and journals, in 60 languages. Information searching takes a big $1.5-billion bite (roughly 12%) of the research and development funds spent annually in the United States. In fact many companies find it easier to duplicate research already performed, rather than spend time and money on a lengthy search for lost reports. Lord Rayleigh pointed out in 1884 that: "Re-discovery in the library may be a more difficult and uncertain process than the first discovery in the Laboratory."

Further, even though there is a plethora of printed technical matter around today, the quantity will double about every eight and one-half years. The estimate for the late 1960's, is 120-million pages of text material published annually.

Many computer-aided information retrieval systems have been developed to break this paper log-jam. For example, the American Society of Metals, in its literature center at Western Reserve University in Cleveland, Ohio, is magnetically taping 12,000 summaries of articles and books per year on the subject of metallurgy. Through this system it is possible to make literature searches at the rate of 100,000 an hour. And exceeding this, a government agency has a system which can produce and exhibit any one of a hundred million randomly-filed documents within ten seconds. Given a person's social security number, the system could, for instance, produce a biographical sketch of anyone in the United States in less than half a minute.

Because the storage of large quantities of printed material represents a problem in itself, devices have been developed which, through microphotographics, reduce the printed page 100 to 1 or more. In this way 5,000 books the size of this one are stored in a compact unit taking up a volume of one cubic foot. Any particular page in these books could be directly selected in response to a coded signal in about one second. The page could be projected onto microfilm, electrostatically printed, transmitted to locations thousands of miles away or viewed on a television screen.

Another area in which machines are helping the scientist-engineer is the laboratory. In essence, the laboratory is becoming automated to the same degree as the factory. Machines direct the progress of an experiment, analyze the data generated, print out or graph the information, and then compare the measured results with predicted results. In some cases, computers decide on the best way to perform an experiment. Automation is taking hold, not only in the industrial test laboratory—which is characterized by large numbers of repetitive measurements anyhow—but also in the research laboratory. There are many experiments in the purest of research activities which require thousands of measurements as, for instance, X-ray diffraction analysis to determine the structure of a complicated crystal. The task of synthesizing insulin, which took ten years, could have been accomplished in one-tenth the time today with automated chemical analyzers and computer-aided reduction of data.

Perhaps the most significant current day machines are those involved with automated design. The traditional tools of the design engineer—his drawing board, desk calculator, slide rule and even pencil and paper—are rapidly following the shoemaker's hand tools. At first glance it would appear that the design process would be about the last thing to be automated, since it is so closely associated with personal creativity. But engineer/computer teams have already developed airplanes, automobiles, clothing, highway designs, plus many others. Perhaps it is more correct to say that the computer has aided in this design in a sort of man-machine intellectual partnership.

The basis for the advanced type of machine-aided design being discussed here is the graphic console, connected to a computer, plus the light pen. Instead of drawing in the conventional way using pencil, T-square, compass, triangles, and French curves, the engineer sits in front of a cathode-ray tube, similar to a television screen, and draws (really sketches) with the light pen. The light pen, the size and shape of a fountain pen, contains a photoelectric cell which, when held to a spot or line on the cathode-ray tube face, causes the spot or line to follow movements of the pen. Words have been written on the face of the screen in this manner and were read and understood by the computer. But this is done at present only to show that it can be accomplished. No doubt, if such written communication is a convenient form of instructing a computer, this technique will be developed further.

In creating a design, an engineer draws shapes on the face of the tube. The shapes are then converted into numerical form by the computer and stored in the machine's memory. For example, the engineer can draw four rather wiggly lines and, by pushing buttons, tell the computer to straighten out the lines and form a perfect square. The computer does this and "remembers" the square in algebraic rectangular coordinates. He can also tell the computer to select the larger or smaller square, create a number of squares, rotate the squares, or change the squares into rectangles. The engineer can also ask the computer to tell (on a digital readout or the tube face) how long a particular line is. Once the computer has the sketched design well in mind, it can present, either separately or simultaneously, top, front, side, and perspective views plus cross-sectional views at designated places. Changing a line in any of these views will automatically present a corresponding new line in the other views.

If the engineer wants to experiment with a new idea, he can push a button and store his old drawings in the computer's memory until he is ready to look at them again. Complex shapes such as a turbine blade or a propeller can be roughly sketched and, by telling the computer the formula for the curve, the correct picture will be displayed. Once displayed, pictures can be made, the information can be presented digitally on tapes (for later insertion into a machine tool), or, as mentioned previously, transmitted to some remote video receiver.

The machine also can perform stress analyses on the various parts of a design. And, if an excessive load is added to a particular portion of a design the computer can "re-design" the part and other affected parts until the load can be carried. It is presently feasible (although never done), to design an automobile engine in this manner. The engine could then operate in animated-cartoon fashion with the pistons moving up and down and the crankshaft rotating. While it is running in this fashion the engineer can enlarge (as with a zoom lens) a particular section of the engine, stop the engine, change a dimension on a part which interferes with another at high speed, and start the engine working again to check the effectiveness of his alteration.

When we consider all of today's machines, we note one type—the product of the last five minutes, so to speak—which overshadows the others in current significance and future potential: the general purpose electronic computer. In the time scale we have selected, yesterday's machines extended man's power of sight (the telescope, microscope, and television), hearing (the stethoscope, telephone, and radio), and so on. In the last five minutes, as the third broad stride was taken, man's brain was augmented and his intellect extended. While originally conceived of as fast, but simple calculators, these computers are being increasingly used in practically every aspect of human endeavor: in the design of weapons and highways; in the training of physicians; and many more areas too numerous to mention.

Charles Babbage, an English mathematician, observed in the early 1800's that the progress of physical science was being hampered by excessive mental labor. He conceived of a machine—the prototype of the modern day electronic computer—to reduce mental labor in much the same way as other devices being developed at that time reduced physical labor. He spent a major portion of his time and personal fortune figuring out how to build his "analytical engine" which would calculate and print mathematical tables such as logarithms and tables of squares. The machine, if ever completed, would have been a supermechanism of 50,000 wheels and gears, plus many clutches, levers, cams, and the like.

People were interested, and the English Parliament supported his earlier efforts by granting him about $75,000 in 1812. But actualization of Babbage's vision had to await the development of reliable and lightning-fast electronic components. He was on the right track and his designs, left in five volumes of engineering sketches and notes, are duplicated, in principle at least, in the current-day general purpose computer. Incidentally, Babbage "programmed" his machine through its ingenious mechanical memory, using punched cards. The punch card was developed about 1801 by Joseph Jacquard for use in patterning brocaded silk on looms. These cards were adapted to their current use by Dr. Herman Hollerith in 1886.

I wonder why Jules Verne, a contemporary of Babbage, did not use the "analytical engine" as a theme in one of his science-fiction stories. Perhaps he felt that while the nuclear engine of his *Nautilus* submarine was credible, a "thinking" engine was beyond credibility even for a science-fiction tale.

In any event it was not until World War II, the time of many new developments, that the first large-scale digital computer, called the Automatic Sequence-Controlled Calculator, was constructed. Development of this general purpose computer was completed by the IBM Corporation and Harvard University engineers in 1944. It was an electromechanical device using relays as the "on-off" switches.

It should be mentioned that a special purpose automatic digital computer was built prior to the IBM-Harvard machine. Dr. George R. Stiblitz of the Bell Telephone Laboratories developed, in 1939, a relay operated computer to solve equations for analyzing alternating current and electrical circuits. Dr. Stiblitz's device, which he called the "Complex Computer," represented another "first" as it had a satellite input-output station in a remote location. That is, while the computing panels remained in the Laboratories in New York, mathematicians at Dartmouth College in New Hampshire gave problems to the machine via teletype and received the answers via teletype in New Hampshire.

The first electronic computer to use vacuum tubes as counters came about a year later. It was called ENIAC (Electronic Numerical Integrator and Computer) and was designed by Drs. John W. Mauchly and J. Presper Eckert Jr., at the University of Pennsylvania.

As can be imagined, the ENIAC was clumsy by today's trim standards for computers. Completed shortly after the close of the war, it occupied a room 30 x 50 feet, contained 18,200 vacuum tubes, and weighed 30 tons. Also, it was not noted for its high reliability. Rather it tended to break down frequently and without warning. But it did do useful work and solved a problem for the atomic program in two months that otherwise would have taken a hundred man-years of effort with the conventional desk calculator then used. However, modern computers can perform the same task in hours or even minutes.

Today's computers represent the work of many people, who use mainly the pioneering ideas of the late mathematician, John von Neumann. Also, Vannevar Bush, foreseeing a fuller potential, helped the computer play a broader role than merely doing arithmetic problems and solving technical equations. In 1951 the Bureau of the Census used UNIVAC I (Universal Automatic Computer) for statistics related to the 1950 census. The machine, incidentally, was retired in 1963.

The computer industry became big business, and grew from about 300 digital computers in 1955, to a total of 4,700 in practical use in the United States at the close of 1961. By 1964 the figure climbed to 14,500, representing a four-billion-dollar investment. Conservative industry projections are that this number will double by 1969.

Of course, computers are not all of the same kind. They fall into two major divisions; *analog* and *digital*, and other minor ones. The analog computer solves problems by working with physical quantities or conditions which vary, such as temperature, length, flow, voltage, and pressure. These computers are used mainly in scientific research. In the digital computer, information is represented in discrete form (yes or no, 1 or 0, on or off, etc.) and calculations are made with these binary numbers in much the same way we calculate by hand with the ten-digit system. A new breed of computer that holds great promise is the "hybrid" which combines the desirable features of both the analog and digital computers.

Some computers are *on-line* in such manner that the input and output devices are wired directly to the computer, as in a process control system. Other computers are *off-line* and the inputs and outputs are on punched cards, perforated tape, or magnetic tape which are transferred from the source to the computer by hand.

Some computers are *general purpose* and are used for various types of data processing, the nature of which often is not known before the computer is designed. Other computers are *special purpose* and are built to process specific type of data such as navigating a space vehicle, controlling temperatures and pressures of liquids, or handling commercial and personal banking operations.

Computers are also classified as small, medium, or large. Recently there is a tendency to build computer equipment in "families" or in modular form so that a small installation may use only a few basic pieces of equipment or larger installations may contain many of these same standard cabinets, operating consoles, and peripheral equipment at remote locations.

Large computers are expensive and the hourly rates for their use may run into hundreds of dollars. When an operation to be performed by the computer is well prepared and straightforward, the time required is relatively brief. But frequently the user has to sit down and decide, as a result of the information already furnished by the computer, where to proceed next. Typically, the user may take an hour for his "homework," then go to the computer with his prepared problem and get his answer in a fraction of a second and then repeat the cycle. Obviously, monopolization of a computer costing millions of dollars in this fashion is an unacceptable practice. To solve the dilemma of fast computer and slow human, the practice is now to provide "multiple-access" or time-sharing, a practice used extensively in telephone switchboard operation. In this way, many users can share in the use of a single computer.

Universities furnish examples of community use of computers. Professors and students, or teams of users, at perhaps fifty different locations, utilize a centralized computer. Each location is equipped with a teletypewriter which is "dialed" into the computer, and a two-way communication is established. While the computer has buffering equipment to store incoming information until it is ready for it, to the user the operation is essentially instantaneous because of the billionth-second calculating speed of the computer.* As soon as the problem is presented the teletypewriter click-clacks the answer. For good measure, the centralized university computer may ask the student: "Have you asked your girl to the senior prom?" or "Don't forget to vote next Tuesday." Also, if the student has some spare time, he can ask the computer for some tutorial help.

To illustrate, a medical student may request a diagnosis exercise. The computer will describe, for instance, the condition of a patient brought into the emergency ward of a hospital. The student then tells the computer what initial action is to be taken, the clinical test to be made, and so forth. At the end of the exercise the student is to diagnose the disease or malfunction. If the student makes a serious error or uses bad judgment, the computer may print a statement like:

You know John [incidentally the student has to introduce himself to the computer which, in turn, always calls him by name], you are lucky to have gotten this far in your medical career. But don't press your luck. If your handling of this case is representative, you are not going to last long.

Of course, the computer does not make these statements up by itself; a professor puts them in the memory bank to be used when a student exhibits a certain pattern in answering inquiries or in putting questions to the computer. Chances are, the "stock" observations made by the computer would be exactly the same if the

---

* If a man added two 5-digit numbers every minute for 24 hours a day from the time of Christ, he would by now have accomplished as much work as the computer could do in one second. In another decade computers are projected to operate at speeds of a trillionth of a second.

student were being examined in person by the professor who programmed the computer.

Computers can do more than conventional arithmetic operations and help students with school work. They can also perform logic functions. That is, they not only can tell you "A + B = C" but "If either A or B is present, but neither C nor D, then E is true"; or "If A follows B, but only after an E, then all G's should be H's." When words, phrases, or war-time situations are substituted for the letters, it can be seen that manipulation of these logic functions take on increased significance.

In sum, computers can calculate mathematical relations among numbers and perform logical operations using symbols. They can perform these calculations and reasoning operations at literally the speed of lightning. There will be no attempt here to describe the inner workings of computers; there are many excellent books written in popular language for the non-technically oriented reader. In keeping with the theme of this book, it is the significance and impact of these intellect-aiding machines on man's place in the increasingly mechanized scheme of things that are of immediate interest to us.

Most people have been left with the impressions formed during the earliest days of computers. They are unaware of more recent developments. The uninformed often say a computer is merely a big adding machine that manipulates figures as it has been told to by its human programmer. They also point out that when computers solve a complex problem, the route taken is clearly marked out in map-like fashion. These belittling statements are not true. Modern computers have means built into them to solve vaguely defined problems which require decision-making at many points before the problem can be solved. To aid in making these decisions, vast quantities of factual information are stored in the computer's memory or, additionally, the computer can draw on outside stored information or, in desperation, call for further information from the user as required.

There is a point concerning today's machines that warrants closer examination; this primarily concerns the speed with which new devices are being developed. Compare transistors and integrated circuits, for example. When transistors first appeared they were crude affairs produced in odd corners of a plant. They were assembled by inexperienced workers who, in turn, were directed by bewildered engineers drafted from totally unrelated work. To further add to the confusion, there was initially little or no specialized equipment for the manufacture of transistors. As a consequence, transistors themselves were developed at a slower rate than were the devices using the transistors.

Today the situation is reversed. Skilled workers, knowledgeable engineers, plus excellent manufacturing facilities and tools already exist. As a result, new integrated circuits are developed faster than the equipments which use them. Nevertheless, the transistor with one foot dragging behind has carried the electronic industry along at breathtaking speed. New equipment using transistors, such as the second generation computer, was more compact, more reliable, and less expensive. The transistor did this by replacing elements in the first generation of computer electronic equipment on only a one-for-one basis. Now the integrated circuit, representative of the third generation of computer, replaces all sorts of individual electronic elements, including transistors, on a hundred-to-one or more basis.

To summarize, the impact of transistors on the field of electronics, while great, will hardly compare to the impact that integrated circuits portends for the electronics industry. Needless to say, the ripples—or more properly, the shock waves—from this latter development will spread to touch us all.

To what kind of equipment will the third, and succeeding, generations of electronic components be applied? No doubt there will be many, but we can cite two examples: machines that hear and those that see.

Machines that hear and see. Notice the absence of qualifying quotation marks around these faculties previously possessed by living things only. Certainly we are referring to dybological hearing and seeing, but there is not the uncertainty here as there is in the case of machine "thinking." A telephone receiver or microphone hears, but only in the sense of converting sounds into electrical impulses. The machines we are talking about here recognize spoken words or other distinctive sound patterns and act in some predetermined manner, in response to the spoken information.

An experimental machine has been developed by the IBM Corporation, named "Shoebox" (because of its size and shape). It recognizes up to sixteen words, including the ten digits. The machine is connected to a calculator and an operator merely voices numbers and commands such as "plus" or "minus" into a microphone. The Shoebox hears these instructions, in that they are stored in its memory. At the command "total," the machine completes its calculations and provides the answer to the arithmetic problem. The circuitry for Shoebox contains 31 transistors; fewer than two for each word it recognizes. Word discrimination is based on phonetic differences between words: the existence or absence of spoken sounds as well as weak or strong fricative sounds and their relative location in the word.

Similar work was done at the Air Force Cambridge Research Laboratories (AFCRL). The work at AFCRL suggests the possibility of a computer being able to answer back "in kind" to its operators. By-products of this experimentation are: simple language translation in which a word spoken in one language is recognized by the computer, translated into a second language and typed out in printed form; individual speaker recognition in which the computer is able to identify the speaker from the characteristics of his speech; and an adaptive program which enables the computer to automatically adjust itself to a different speaker's manner of talking. The vocabulary of the experimental device was 83 spoken words, requiring one and a half seconds for recognition. With larger and faster machines, the vocabulary can be considerably larger and the response time considerably decreased to match the speed of a fast speaker.

Much more work has been done with machines that see (a number of which are now commercially available), than with machines that hear. While there is little need to instruct machines orally, there is considerable need for a faster way of feeding printed or graphic material into computers. Generally, the input-output ratio of computers is such that they absorb and digest vast quantities of information but produce a relatively small output. Even large outputs are handled with relative ease by use of high-speed printers or visual display equipment. The problem rests squarely with the input. Conventionally, computer inputs take the form of punched cards, punched paper tape, and magnetic tape. In effect, the input media is prepared one letter, or number, at a time at about typewriter speed.

To solve this computer input bottleneck, visual readers have been developed. In general, these readers are TV in reverse. That is, instead of projecting a picture on a cathode ray tube (CRT), as for instance a page of print, the picture is sensed by the CRT. Scanning of the picture is controlled by the computer into which the desired information is being fed. By doing its own scanning the computer can accomplish its own reading a thousand times faster than would be the case if an operator traced each line with a probe.

The Philco Corporation has developed a general purpose print reader which reads typed or printed pages without the use of stylized or magnetic ink letters or numbers (as is the case in most bank check readers). Documents to be fed into the computer are merely stacked in a pile and the machine then transports each page to the optical reader, converts the printed words to machine language, and writes the information onto magnetic tapes, paper tapes, or punched cards. The reader even corrects its own mistakes and inserts the correction in the proper places in the text. It can re-read unclear or smudged characters directly without scanning the whole page. The machine is not confused when the type-face changes or if the lines of type are uneven. The reader is no slow poke; it can read about 24,000 words per minute. Roughly, the Philco General Purpose Print Reader could read and convert to machine language 60 pages of this book every minute.

Many companies other than Philco make optical character-recognition systems. Among them are IBM, General Precision, National Cash Register, Univac, Rainbow Engineering, Radio Corporation of America, and Sylvania.

While a person recognizes a letter or number "all at once," some of these machines look for more than 300 different bits of information on each character. In most cases the machine readers can make out characters unintelligible to a human. Further, the more the machine reads, the more it "learns" about the characteristics of each number or letter. It ultimately is able to identify a letter even if it is placed upside down. Present day machine readers not only can handle the various styles of English type, including upper and lower-case letters, but other alphabets as well, including the Chinese alphabet with its tens-of-thousands of different characters. It is true that human abilities have been duplicated in machines, but we must view these developments in a proper perspective. To illustrate, a shovel can dig much faster than a human hand. Yet we do not claim that a shovel is a more wonderful device than the hand. (The city boy bragged to his country cousin how much better his bicycle was than the farm boy's cow. To make his point the city boy said, "You would look silly riding the cow." "Not as silly," answered the country boy, "as you would look trying to milk the bicycle.")

Nevertheless, the fearfully asked question—"Are the machines taking over?"—has not been answered. It would be reassuring to say, "Of course not." But the true answer, at least for the immediate future, hinges on a very fine point. The machines are not taking over in the manner popularly displayed on TV and in the movies; rather they are "intruding" themselves into our lives to an ever-increasing degree.

To explain. Originally a person was directly and physically related to the product he designed and manufactured. Then hand tools were developed which, ever so slightly, separated the worker from his work; then machine tools were built which further widened the gap. Currently, as we have seen, machines are now designing still newer machines. And so this trend—the intrusion of machines between man and his work—continues at a rather fast pace.

Another example of this trend is the process of instructing computers in programming. The first computers were programmed completely by humans. This is essentially true even today. But the newer, larger computers cannot be left idle while instructions are prepared. To speed up the process, smaller computers are programmed to tell the larger computer what to do. No doubt the trend will continue with yet more computers added to the chain of events between human input and the final result.

When a person directly programmed the one computer which provided the final results, the accuracy of the output could be checked by the individual because he was intimately familiar with the input. While a bit more difficult, he can also verify the results when an extra computer is inserted into the computation process. Still, if this intrusion extends much further it will not be possible to check results. Paradoxically, this problem is being resolved by inserting additional computers into the chain of events to make certain that no errors are fed into the primary computer. (It is interesting to note that to insure the computers against making errors themselves, due to failure of some part, the computers' circuits have been "triplicated" and the final output represents a majority vote among them. That is, if the output from one circuit is different from that of the other two, it is assumed to have failed and its output is overridden or ignored.)

In brief, more relevant than the question of the machines "taking over" is man's need to place more confidence in the performances of the machines he has created. Stated simply, man is becoming more dependent upon machines than upon nature and his own abilities. The situation is similar to that of a man in an iron lung. Things are satisfactory as long as the machinery works. This situation was brought home with great impact during the November 1965 blackout of the northeastern states when the electrical power network failed.

It is difficult to think of the impact of today's machines on ourselves and our way of life without worrying somewhat about what comes next. Tools, such as hammers and saws, to help a person perform manual tasks are accepted, but having a machine as an intellectual partner is—at least on the surface—disconcerting. For example, the personal relationship between scientist and laboratory assistant, or the engineer and draftsman, is fast disappearing. It takes two to have a personal relationship and as we have seen the laboratory assistant and draftsman are being replaced by their mechanical equivalents. There is a relationship of sorts but it is turning into a man-machine relationship. Whether this mechanical relationship becomes a dehumanizing force is yet to be seen.

Chapter Seven

Machines Mimic Nature

To comprehend a living thing
past any doubts
You cancel first the living spirit
out.
The parts lie in the hollow of
your hand
You only lack the living spirit you
banned.

—Goethe

Perhaps the widespread use of nature's answers to solve man's technical problems had to await the formation of a working team.

Until recently, one individual—a biologist, for example, may have seen the solution to the housefly's flight stabilization problem. But he was unaware that another individual—an engineer—was faced with the problem of developing a lightweight, simple, and accurate substitute for the heavy, complex and error prone gyroscope. Somehow, these two individuals did get together (just how they did is hard to imagine) and the biologist pointed out to the engineer the vibrating rods on a fly's head. In this way, the engineer was presented with a working model of a device which, chances are, he otherwise never would have imagined.

Just as the clinical physician and the engineer joined forces to solve more quickly the riddles blocking a healthier and longer life, another new team has been formed: a trio composed of biologist, mathematician, and engineer. Or more correctly, the biologist is joining an already existing partnership of mathematician and engineer. Recent events indicate it is fortunate that scientists, familiar with the inner workings of nature, are making their presence felt in the development of newer machines and devices.

Whether an engineer would go on designing equipment successfully without thinking about how nature would produce the same function is a debatable point. In any event, the biologist has un-

121

covered many of nature's very efficient designs which lend themselves admirably to the engineers' needs.

In the past, the engineer created instruments for the life scientist with no expectation of a technical contribution in return. But when the biologist used an oscilloscope to record the supersonic shrieks of a bat, for instance, the similarity between these high frequency energy pulses and radar signals quickly became apparent. Why work separately, the engineer and biologist realized, when there was so much to be accomplished by working together?

The advanced mathematician saw that his new techniques were specifically suited for dealing with organic types of complexity whether found in living things or in machines (such commonness in function and characteristics is one of the foundations of cybernetics). The organized complexity we are speaking of in machines involves mainly robots, self-learning, and self-organizing systems. These machines are known collectively as automata.

While the biologist, mathematician, and engineer have joined together as a team, it is apparent that each may have a different attitude concerning the team's goal. The engineer likes to produce a device to perform a function; he wishes to satisfy his creative urges. Basically, he feels the design should be as simple as possible and yet workable. The biologist on the other hand wants to create designs which will help him unlock the secrets of life. To the biologist, the ideal device is one which performs in the same way living things perform even if the device does this inefficiently. Further, he is happy to leave the mechanics of design to the engineer while he, the biologist, observes and analyzes.

The mathematician is as different in his motivation and desires as the engineer or biologist. He is not primarily interested in the real or the physical regardless of whether it is animate or inanimate. The mathematician likes to deal in symbolic abstractions; to reduce things to a number, letter, or sign. He likes to combine, separate, or otherwise manipulate these representations of real things so the relationships among them can be solved in quiet and uninterrupted seclusion.

Perhaps it is just because the engineer, biologist, and mathematician are extremely different (each 120° out of phase, as it is technically put) that the triumvirate is proving to work out so well. There is no conflict of interest because the areas of interest do not overlap. The three individual areas of interest fit together into a neat whole.

What will fuse the team members into a working group? No doubt it will be the problems that offer a challenge to each member of the trio. This work deals with the use of living things as prototypes for machines which then become physical analogs of complex biological functions. In short, biological knowledge can be applied to solve engineering problems and, once solved, to a better understanding of living systems. Mathematics serves as the catalyst to promote the interchange.

If two areas of scientific effort seemed right for a marriage, they were the fields of biology and electronics. Probably it was a case of opposites attracting one another. While some look at the match as a May-December relationship (electronics is after all so much younger than biology), the union does have all the elements of a successful match; the appearance already of so many offspring attests to that. Maybe the two sciences have existed separately as long as they could, and further progress depended upon a joining of forces.

In the middle and late 1700's, biologists were aware of "animal electricity." Galvani showed that an electric current could cause a muscular reaction in a frog's leg, and others noted that the shocks received from certain fish were electrical in origin. While it seems that electronics engineers and scientists could have worked as they had a little while longer, there was a strong tendency pushing them to become "involved" with biology. The fields of physics and chemistry, both of which started out as purely separate disciplines, later tended to overlap in some of their subject material as in the case of atomic energy. Similarly, biology and electronics are tending to overlap in many of their areas of interest.

An intriguing aspect of biology and electronics which was previously touched upon is the difference in approach the practitioners of each of these sciences take. One seems to zag where the other one zigs. Biology is essentially a "descriptive" science; its goal is to observe and classify the things that can be seen, with hardly any present desire to change anything. On the other hand, electronics engineering is a "creative" science; its goal is to make something that did not exist before or, perhaps, change something that does exist. The emphasis in biology is finding "how" the various physical processes operate. In electronics, the emphasis is in finding "why" physical processes operate the way they do. Biologists approach their subject from a practical point of view and then go on to theoretical explanation; electronics engineers approach their subject from a theoretical point of view and then go on to practical demonstration. Biologists work from a foundation of living things they can dissect and visually examine; electronics engineers work from a foundation of mathematics and then proceed to develop useful devices to calculate, communicate, control, catalog, entertain, and so on.

As often happens when the conditions for the emergence of a new technology are ripe, it takes but one individual to precipitate otherwise loosely related generalities into a simple, crystal clear idea. The individual we refer to is Air Force Major Jack Steele; and the idea is called bionics.

Major Steele started out to become an engineer, but his interests eventually led him to obtain a medical degree, to become a psychiatrist, and finally a flight surgeon. While performing the duties of a research psychiatrist at Wright Field Aerospace Research Laboratory, Steele and his colleagues derived the word bionics. The word seemed to evolve naturally from the Greek, *bios* (meaning "life") and the suffix *ics* (meaning "after the manner of"). Captain Leslie E. Knapp, of the Bionics Section of ASD, Wright Patterson Air Force Base, defines bionics as "the science and technology devoted to the study and analysis of living systems and the physical realization of the more sophisticated of these functions." In spite of this definition, the popular conception—or misconception—is that the term bionics is a combination of biology and electronics. Actually, this latter field of effort is called, logically, bioelectronics.

While bionics, in its originally conceived sense, is synonymous with the term dybology (which was coined at about the same time) there seems to be no conflict. At least for the present, bionics is used in a relatively narrow sense to describe the work of scientists who use biological systems as models for machines. Dybology, on the other hand, tends to be used to denote anything life-like or natural like, but artificially created. There has been no conflict to date in the use of the two words nor is any anticipated.

The purpose of bionics was summed up nicely by Dr. Harvey E.

Savely, Director of Life Sciences, Air Force Office of Scientific Research, when in 1960 he told the group assembled for the first
bionics symposium: "In living things problems of organized complexity have been solved with a success that invites our wonder and
admiration. It is natural, therefore, that we look to these successful
inventions in nature for clues, as well as inspirations, for new classes
of man-made machines with greatly increased capabilities."

In the early 1960's many engineers and scientists noted that while
they were simulating nature's handiwork, as far as function was
concerned, their hardware designs suffered greatly when compared
to living organisms; the living systems were considerably smaller,
had higher sensitivities and reliabilities, and were more adaptable.
As an example, the radar warning device we put in our automobiles
to outfox the state highway police are clumsy compared to the
equivalent devices in the noctuid moth. The moth's ear requires
only two nerve fibers to detect the high frequency sonar signals of
a hungry bat on the prowl.

While we are discussing the precision and sensitivity of natures'
creatures, some other examples may prove interesting. The rattlesnake, for instance, has an infrared sensing organ in the pit between
his nostril and eye which can detect differences in temperature one-
thousandth of a degree centigrade. In tests, the rattlesnake would
seek out and strike the warmer of two bodies which had this small
heat difference.

There is a breed of moth in Trinidad with a sense of smell so
keen that a male can detect a female who is a mile away. This keen-
ness represents essentially the ability to smell a single molecule of
the female scent.

Bats can fly in dark caves at fast speeds and yet avoid hanging
obstacles which are only a fraction of an inch in diameter. Bats of
the family Vespertilionidae beep 10- to 100-times a second at frequencies up to 120,000 cycles per second (they can hear sounds up
to 200,000 cycles per second, or ten times higher in frequency than
humans). The "beeper" by which the bat generates his sonar signals weighs only a few grains and, on a relative energy level basis,
the bat can produce more noise than the ordinary human can by
shouting.

Creatures of the sea provide other keys for unlocking nature's secrets. Because man is inclined to work and does engage in combat under the ocean's surface, study of the natural inhabitants of these watery depths provides useful knowledge. Already much information has been extracted and applied toward the advancement of commercial marine endeavor as well as submarine warfare.

A much publicized investigation dealt with the porpoise's speed and wakeless maneuvering. The study revealed how the porpoise's complex skin structure reduces the water's drag on its body at high speed. Not as well publicized, however, was the subsequent finding that for bodies larger than a porpoise, such as a large torpedo or a submarine, the speed-enhancing, anti-turbulence principle does not work well. But the studies continue. Also intriguing is the porpoise's ability to detect and identify objects at distances up to two miles away.

There is a specie of fish found in tropical waters that can detect a current of 200-billionths of an ampere per square centimeter of its body. Using this electronic detection capability it can discriminate between glass rods differing in diameter by less than one-tenth of an inch.

The cuttlefish controls its buoyancy in a similar way to the system used in a submarine. When the submarine is to dive, the commander calls for filling the ballast tanks with sea water; when the vessel is to surface, the water is displaced from the tanks by compressed air. But the cuttlefish performs these operations more subtly. Instead of a compressed-air pump, the cuttlefish sets up an osmotic force by a difference of salt concentration between the fish's cuttlebone fluid and its blood. With any change in sea pressure, the osmotic pressure changes in order to balance the sea pressure.

We tend to view the lowly sand flea with smug superiority— assuming we look hard enough to see him in the first place—as he erratically jumps about. But our respect for this little creature grows extensively when we realize that at least one species, the Talitrus saltator, can steer himself to the seashore on the basis of the moon's position. An equivalent electronic guidance system which could perform the same complex navigational computations would probably weigh about five pounds.

Thus while progress has been made in using biological systems as living prototypes for the design of new machines, the effort so far represents the proverbial drop in the bucket. There is already a large backlog of work to be done in biological engineering. This work includes the study and design of actuators based on muscles; brainlike computers and sensor designs based on biological organs; energy cycles for machines based on metabolism of fuels; and production and fabrication of complex machines based on genetics.

Some of the few drops in the bionic's bucket can be seen in contracts already awarded by the USAF Electronics Technology Laboratory. These contracts call for: studies of human perception in order to build a machine for avoiding collision by judging distances; building an artificial high efficiency muscle to lift heavy loads; devising methods for communicating with an overloaded pilot through his sense of touch rather than orally or visually; the study of neuronic networks by mathematical theory and computer simulation; the development of goal-directed systems which are able to form their own components and circuitry and which are capable of creating mutations under controlled conditions.

Another Government agency that has conducted study programs in the useful applications of life sciences since about 1956 is the Office of Naval Research, averaging about thirty projects at a given time. Information which can be useful in electronic design is sought. For example, there are studies in animal migration, especially birds and turtles, communication studies with porpoises, and sonar in bats. In general, studies of this type tend not only toward cross-fertilization within the various sciences (which incidentally number more than 1,150) but also to unite the various life and physical sciences by having their practitioners work toward common objectives. These goals center around the need for better means of communication, detection, guidance and control, navigation, and computation.

With the development of solid-state physics and microminiaturization, the electronics engineer is on speaking terms with systems that are comparable to biological systems. New equipment contains components which, considering their number, size, function and methods of handling are quickly becoming comparable to biological systems. (While writing this book I received a report which described a problem of oxidation in a gold-aluminum bond of a microelectronic circuit. The diagnosis of the condition—known ominously as the "purple plague"—used equipment and techniques that would warm the heart and bring a knowing smile to the lips of any pathologist.)

A major key for penetrating the secrets of nature is the simulation of nerve cells. Nerve cells, together with their processes, are called neurons. The neurons serve as the basic components in an animal's nervous system. If complex sensing and intellectual activity are to be extensively simulated in man-built machines, an artificial neuron seems to be an essential element in any progress toward this end. Many private laboratories in industry and the universities, plus government laboratories, are developing both physical—including chemical, electronic, and mechanical—as well as mathematical models of the biological neuron. These models or analogs are variously called artificial neurons, neuromimes, neuristors, and artrons. The particular facets of the neuron which are of interest to the engineer are its role in manipulating, coding, processing, and transmitting information.

Neuron models are built with two end objectives in mind depending upon the group responsible for the development. One group tries to make the dybological neuron as close as possible, in function at least, to its biological counterpart. This is done to better understand the body and its operation. The other group builds neurons which serve as the key elements in perceptive and self-learning machines. The main interest is with the machines and in these cases neurons are treated no differently than are other components.

It is interesting to note that the first group of biologists and engineers to work with physiological systems call their efforts "wet work" or "bloody bionics." This is to differentiate their area of endeavor from the mechanical hardware or "dry work" of the second group. The second group is product-oriented, and primarily interested in designing new types of machines to perform useful functions.

Machines which could read in the fully human sense of the word were described in the preceding chapter. However these machines are programmed to read. In other words, each letter is scanned in a methodical fashion and the results (variations in energy reflected back into the scanning CRT) are matched with a complete set of letters previously stored in the machine. When the characteristics of the letter that is read corresponds with the characteristics of a stored letter, it is then identified by comparison circuits. This is equivalent to trying a number of keys in a lock until the right one is found.

Machines have now been developed which can be "taught" to read (or automatically identify objects or patterns, as well as letters) rather than simply be programmed to read. These pattern recognizing machines (where the pattern may also be a photograph or the sounds in a spoken word) are named perceptrons by their developer, Frank Rosenblatt of the Cornell Aeronautical Laboratory. The Mark I Perceptron, demonstrated in mid-1960, consisted of a "sensory unit" of photocells which viewed the pattern shown to the machine; "association units" that contained the machine's memory; and "response units" that visually displayed the machine's pattern recognition response. In effect, the machine conformed very closely with the way human beings are thought to recognize what they see.

Perceptrons are taught to discriminate between different shaped objects and to identify them, without prior knowledge of their form, in much the same way that a child learns. For example, an "A" may be held in front of the machine's mosaic of light sensitive phototubes. The machine is asked to identify the letter. Unless it makes a lucky guess, the machine never having seen the letter "A" before will give the wrong response and perhaps call it a "T." The human trainer then operates controls which in effect tell the machine that the letter is an "A," and not a "T." The same process is repeated for another letter. After a few trials, the machine starts to identify the letters correctly more times than not. When it identifies the letter correctly the trainer does nothing. When the machine gives a wrong answer, it is informed that it has erred. This is called "corrective training" and is more effective (on the Mark I Perceptron at least) than the alternative method of "reinforcement training." In this latter method the trainer informs the machine not only of its errors (by pushing a punishment button) but also its successes (by pushing a reward button). If the trainer were to try to trick the machine after it had learned to identify a letter by falsely calling the letter "F" a "B," for instance, the machine would still call the letter "F" correctly on the next try with the "corrective" method.

The perceptron-type machines are being developed (mostly with Military funds) to handle such tasks as recognizing and spotting missile bases or military airplanes in aerial reconnaissance photographs. These machines are also put to work in space programs. Satellites send back photos with machine-gun rapidity. It has been estimated that the analysis of photos produced in one hour by a single satellite would require tens of thousands of man hours. When fully developed, perceptron machines can search and identify targets of military value from photographs at a rate that would be a blur to the human eye.

If, therefore, machines can be taught to read and identify photographs, perhaps they can be taught more complex functions. This challenge is being accepted by many in the field of bionics. Teams of scientists, engineers, and mathematicians are directing their efforts toward machines that can learn to solve problems and also handle vague or poorly defined situations. Machines capable of learning geometric symbols can be modified to navigate over the surface of planets without human control or to repair damaged equipment in locations too hazardous for humans. Of course, we must recognize that the word "learn" generally refers to an animal function just as "think" does. But if we concern ourselves with the result of the function rather than how the function is accomplished there should be no conflict in meanings.

This is not to deny that similarities with animals do exist even in "how" machines are conditioned to react to stimulating patterns. To the extent that animal learning processes are understood, which is far from complete, similarities exist both functionally and physically.

Part of learning is the recognition and identification of patterns of light, sounds, touch, and so forth. The learning process is also one of building upon past experiences. For example, after a child is made aware that a certain formation of lines is an "A" the child can easily recognize and identify this same formation in a block letter or in a Roman style letter with varying thickness, lines, and serifs. Perhaps in the case of an Old English style letter the child has to be assured that the more complex formation is still an "A."

The same would be true of a machine. But once learned, extreme variations are easily recognized by both machine and child.

But we still have not explained how a machine is taught or, for that matter, how a child "recognizes and identifies." We certainly can hypothesize that the alphabet learning process of the child involves his eyes and his brain; or, more specifically, the optical cells in his eye and the neural cells in his brain. Somehow the image seen by his eye and transmitted to his brain evokes the response, "Yes, the letter is an A." With this hardly detailed example to follow, let us try to see how a machine could be made to perform the same feat.

The input and output of our analogous learning machine is quite simple. On the input end we can hold up a card with the letter "A" in front of a camera-like lens. On the output end we can have a series of lights, one for each letter of the alphabet. When the machine illuminates the proper light it will in effect have said, "Yes, the letter is an 'A.' " (Of course, the machine could be made to say the same thing vocally in a child's voice but that is hardly necessary in our example.)

When the child looks at the letter "A," he does so "all at once." That is, he does not scan it as he would in reading a line of type. Nor, for that matter, do we wish to have the machine scan. Identification in this manner, which was described in the preceding chapter, does not lend itself to the type of "learning" being discussed here. Therefore, in order for the machine to also see a letter "all at once" we must display the image conventionally through a single lens, as in the human eye, and have the image impinge on a mosaic of receptors similar to the retina or innermost coating in the back of the human eye. The machine's mosaic is composed of many photocells arranged in a grid fashion. If we stopped at this point in machine complexity, we would have a model of the animated display sign seen for many years on New York's Times Square. In this display, there is a light bulb connected to each photocell. Shining a cartoon on the photocells produces the same image, greatly increased in size, on the face of the sign.

For greater complexity, we will connect each photocell to devices which measure the amount of light each photocell "sees." There is no reason to connect the light measuring devices to the photocells in any logical fashion. You will recall, we are "teaching" the machine, not "programming" it as in the case of the Times Square display sign. Therefore, the connections are randomly made. The light measuring devices are then connected to memory devices which can be adjusted or "weighted" for a given threshold level. In this way, if the amount of light from the measuring devices is above a certain level the memory device will produce, for example, a positive voltage. Conversely, amounts below the threshold level produce a negative voltage.

Groups of memory devices are then connected to summing devices. The summing devices generate an output signal proportional to the algebraic sum of the input voltages from the group of memory devices to which they are connected. If the machine were to be taught only the alphabet, there would be 26 summing devices: one for each letter.

Finally, a comparator examines the output voltage from each summing device and by determining which is the largest, the machine can then indicate which of the patterns already adjusted into its memory devices most closely corresponds to the unknown pattern fed into the "eye" of the machine.

In an actual machine built by Scope, Inc., called the Conflex 1 (for "conditioned reflex"), there were 400 photocells, 5,000 light measuring devices, and 48 summing devices. It is interesting to point out however, that while the Conflex 1 has 240,000 memory cells, the human brain has 10-billion cells.

The Conflex 1, developed for the USAF, quickly learns (in glances of 16.5-thousandths of a second) to recognize and identify up to one hundred variations each of 48 complex patterns. For example, in an "automatic post office test" the machine identified the names of different states whether they were spelled out in full or abbreviated; or whether they were typed, printed, or written in long hand; or whether the names were aligned horizontally or diagonally. In an even more impressive demonstration, the Conflex 1 was exposed to several photographs each of a number of men and women. Then different photos of these same people were shown to the machine, which correctly identified them all. Even when the photos were partially masked by a series of stripes, the machine identified each person correctly. Sometimes a human observer had difficulty in making the same identification. In addition the Conflex 1 correctly identified the two individuals in a purposely made double exposure.

An important aspect of teachable machines lies in their photocell receptors. For the time being, learning machines identify objects of interest only in still pictures or diagrams. In time, these perceptive-type machines will be able to cope with moving objects as, for instance, a radar-type device that can be taught to discriminate between hostile and harmless targets. Of course, today's advanced radars and sonars can separate those targets which are a threat from those which are not. But this faculty lies within the computer—or brain—of the system. A threatening target is identified from calculations of its speed and direction. While such systems are workable, there are more efficient ways of performing this "observational" function.

Oddly enough, the eye/brain combination used in current radars and sonars is patterned after human abilities and in this sense could be considered quite advanced. But being more advanced is not necessarily synonymous to being more efficient. To illustrate, a busy executive can write every routine letter which leaves his office. Yet it is a more efficient practice for his capable secretary to compose and type the more or less standard letters and then submit them for the executive's signature. To use another analogy, it has proven efficient to preprocess foods so that the housewife merely has to add water or, as in the case of TV dinners, just decide when to put them in the oven.

In this same way, bionic researchers are trying to discover nature's way of preprocessing information in the eyes of lower forms of animals, notably the frog and pigeon. While in man the eye transmits only pictures to the brain, in lower animals the eye transmits information which has already been digested somewhat. This is similar to some radars which send information to their computer centers only for moving targets.

By our somewhat biased human standards, we would say that frogs are practically blind. They cannot move their eyes within the sockets. They see only outlines, as in a line cartoon drawing, when observing a scene in which nothing is moving. Nevertheless, the frog's eye has some remarkable properties. It receives, processes, and relays important information to the frog's brain and filters out everything else. The sudden appearance of a shadow, for instance, could indicate danger. The shadow would cause the eye to send a signal to the brain which practically commands a reflexive jump. Or, for example, a bug flying toward a frog is of interest to him; one flying away is not. When the frog is in a hunting state of mind, the range, rate, and bearing information of a potential meal on the wing is processed by eye nerves. With this important information already available (such as the letter composed and typed by the efficient secretary) the frog's eye in effect says: "Yes, that bug is all right to eat." The brain then puts the sticky tongue into action. (But it is the executive who says, "Yes, the letter is all right" and puts his pen into action. In other words, what the executive does in his mind's eye, the frog does in his eye's mind.)

The Radio Corporation of America has built a three and a half foot square, six foot long working model of the frog's retina. The model contains 33,000 electronic components. An advanced version of the model could assist air-traffic controllers to guard against collisions, or could be used in applications where the computer-like eye would detect and help direct an attack against hostile planes or missiles.

Using small electrodes, bionics researchers at the Massachusetts Institute of Technology wire-tapped and traced connections from a frog's retina through the twisted bundles of nerve fibers in the optic tract up to the sight center (the tectum) of the frog's brain. By moving objects of different sizes, shapes, and contrasts at different speeds across the frog's visual field; by stopping the objects or moving them jerkily; by varying the illumination, and so forth, they traced the functions of the frog's eye.

From the five types of ganglion cells in a frog's eye, five feature-extracting functions were distinguished. These features include: boundary detection, dimming detection, contrast movement and change detection, dark convex boundary movement detection, and average light-level measurement.

In the previously mentioned RCA device, built for the Bionics and Computer Branch of the Air Force, there are six retinal layers to process information. Photocells on the outside of the first layer receive light signals. These signals are fed into printed circuits which duplicate the frog's ganglion-cell logic function. An edge is detected if one horizontal receptor in a cross-shaped cell group is exposed to light, and the other is darkened. These signals, plus further logic operations, are fed back through the various layers of the frog's eye model.

A working model of the pigeon's eye has been made by Douglas Aircraft's Astropower Laboratory. The pigeon not only has excellent perceptive abilities but like certain other animals, as the frog, it has the ability to preprocess certain information in its retina. In this way the pigeon provides its brain with a translated image of what its eyes see. Of special interest to the Douglas bionic researchers is the pigeon's ability to detect, within the retina, the motion of an object traveling in a single, given direction. This directional movement detection ability would be desirable in a surveillance radar to detect aircraft flying in a single direction, perhaps inbound. A radar such as this would not clutter up the computers with unwanted data.

The pigeon's retina essentially is a three-layer device. The outer layer contains cones or photoreceptors which convert light images into electrochemical signals. These signals are then transferred to an intermediate layer. This center layer is composed of neurons, or nerve cells, called bi-polars. The bi-polars translate cone signals and transfer them, in a series of pulses, to the third layer formed of retinal ganglion cells. This third layer performs additional operations on the signals it receives and in turn sends out further processed pulses to the brain.

The pulsed code is significant. Early artificial neurons just put out "on" or "off" signals, depending on whether a number of incoming signals were great enough to meet or exceed a given threshold value. By developing an artificial neuron having a pulsed code output and the ability to remember how it recently reacted, the Douglas analog neuron distinguishes itself over previous devices.

When light shines on the photoreceptor field of the artificial pigeon's eye, pulse outputs from the various cells are transformed into audible signals or sometimes displayed on an oscilloscope. The model while still under development demonstrated the ability to detect moving spots and moving edges of certain orientations. It is felt by the Douglas experimenters that unidirectional movement can be obtained by enlarging the artificial retina to 200 cones, the number of bi-polars to 150, and the number of ganglions to 25. An actual pigeon retina has around one million neurons.

The music composed and played by the biologist-mathematician-engineer trio will determine, to a considerable extent, the tunes to which mankind will dance in the future. When carefully considered, the trio's formation comes at a fortuitous time. We have already discussed in man's journey to the dybosphere that he has been able to modify his environment to the extent that he is in turn being modified by the mechanistic environment he has created. Therefore, the conditions of man's future development are set more and more by man himself rather than by strictly natural forces.

In his development of machines man has deviated somewhat from what appears to be a preferred course; the machines were—and are—too mechanistic. They tend to intrude and tear apart organic form and structure. Highly developed technology, as we now know it, creates a state of nervous tension and uneasiness. To some extent we can and must adapt to our machine-world; but to a larger extent we must change the character of our machines. We must humanize our machines to a much greater extent than they are now.

Is humanization of machines a difficult concept to visualize? Not really. An inhuman machine, for instance, is a punch-press that chops-off the fingers of the operator that feeds it. (The thought should be taken in its literal sense; no metaphor is intended.) The machine did not mean to cause the accident nor was doing harm part of the machine's intended purpose. Consider a comparable situation in which there are two humans involved rather than a human and machine. If one of the men is aware of some damage the other could cause inadvertently, he says in effect, "When you see me doing this, be sure you don't do that."

With a machine, the same arrangement can be made. Returning to the punch-press example, we find that—contrary to conditions existing at the turn of the century in which missing fingers, eyes, limbs and more, were the rule rather than the exception—working in a factory now is considerably safer than working in one's home.

How was the industrial environment made safer while still achieving increases in productivity? The answer lies in humanizing the machines: by providing them with sensing devices and—to a limited degree—a communication capability. Through various devices the punch press was told that an operator's hands were in a dangerous position and as a result the machine would not go through its cycle of operation. The machine, in turn, would notify the operator when such things as pressures and temperatures were reaching dangerous levels.

Our punch-press example might be somewhat interesting but it is hardly profound. Taken by itself, the practice of putting safety devices on machine tools would hardly be worth mentioning. But imagine putting safety devices on machines (as opposed to machine tools). This is extremely important because, as implied several times, the machines of the future may transcend most human capabilities by many fold.

In describing the punch-press situation, a sort of communication link was established between the operator and the machine tool. Present communication between man and machine, a computer, for instance, is as actual or literal as it would be between an engineer or scientist and their human assistants who perform calculations. In the future, the communication link between man and machine will have to be sturdier. This is because man will be asking the machine to do more than solve equations or to store and retrieve information. Man will be asking machines to make judgments which call for more or less independent reasoning on the part of the machine. To do this the machine must be aware of what man is aware of and must be able to examine and analyze facts in an objective manner.

Note that I did not say, "know what a man knows or think as a man thinks." To the extent that a man's knowledge can be expressed symbolically, as in mathematics or in checkers and chess moves, computers already know what man knows. And if this knowledge were fed into a machine which reasoned as man does, the digested resulting output would be no better or worse than that produced by another human.

If full machine potential is to be realized in the objective evaluation of various situations that are beyond human capability, the machine must be human-like, yet not entirely a duplicate copy. The point is that machines, to be useful to man, must be designed within two limiting boundaries. Machines cannot be allowed to develop in an uncontrolled evolutionary manner until everything on earth is machine-like. On the other hand, we cannot make machines entirely human-like and then have to compete with essentially duplicates of ourselves for space on an already crowded earth.

Having established the hopeful boundaries for future machine development, we can return to the subject of communication between man and the intelligent machine of the future. Communication between primitive man and his environment was on a strictly physical basis, designed to provide for biological needs. Communication between operator and punch press today is to provide a safeguard against injury to the man and damage to the machine. Communication between man and his mechanistic environment—the dybosphere—tomorrow, will not be as much on a physical basis as on an informational one.

To illustrate, the telephone is as important a part of our environment as was the town well from which water was drawn. As originally conceived the telephone was developed for people to talk to one another. But in many instances today, it is a machine and not a human that gives the weather report, correct time, stock reports, bank balance, or the condition of the highways. The fact that in some of these cases the messages are in the form of prerecorded human voices is of little consequence; in a few years the voices will most likely be synthetized. The important point is that the information provided over the telephone (or the television, or the radio) will be generated essentially in its entirety by machines. And this information will not be simply entertaining as in machine created music, or factual as in a rundown of wind velocity and barometric pressures, but may include a meaningful computer developed "thought for the day."

If therefore, man can communicate with machines which approach or exceed his intelligence, many possibilities arise. Unfortunately, the nature or significance of these possibilities remain clouded because there is no way of knowing in advance what thoughts an intelligent—but purely logical—thinking machine might offer. We may like and profit from the results of such new knowledge or we may be sorry that we opened a Pandora's box of ills. But if the appearance of intelligent machines is inevitable, as I believe it is, then it is wise to temper this intelligence with the same morality and goodness of thinking that characterizes man at his best.

To close the chapter on its opening note, it is fortunate that the biologist has joined forces with the mathematician and engineer. We can rest assured that the machines soon to be developed will be more "natural" and, to an increasing extent, more humanistic. In this way we will be as much at ease in the dybosphere as we were in the biosphere.

Chapter Eight

Intelligent Machines?

The brain is like a computing machine, but there is no machine like the brain.

—Warren McCulloch

Several years ago, in the middle of the computer's horse and buggy era, the question was often asked, "Can machines think?" Today the question asked somewhat timidly is, "Do machines really think?" While the fire has gone out of the debate between the believers (those who say machines can do anything people can do—only better) and the non-believers (those who say machines are at best a poor imitation of people), the arguments—past and current—provide an historical perspective for examining man's place in a machine-dominated world.

The semantics problem should be dealt with first. There are some who say that they cannot answer the question until the term "machine" and "think" are defined. If man is considered a machine, the answer to the question is simply "Yes." Yet if thinking is considered to be possible only in a living brain, then the answer to the question is a straightforward "No."

Much of the semantics problem stems from the vagueness in meaning of the word "think." If the question were asked: "Can a machine pump blood?" the answer would be "Yes." This is because we know explicitly what pumping means both as a process and as a result. Further, we can't deny that a mechanical pump can perform the same function as biological hearts because artificial pumps already have been substituted successfully for their living counterparts. But the functions of thinking, learning, memorizing, understanding, meditating, deliberating, and the rest are difficult to pin

140

down precisely. Even today there is no dictionary definition for any of these functions that would exclude machines from the ability to perform them. The problem is not in knowing how machines or computers solve mathematical problems, store numbers and facts in their memory devices, perceive sounds and photographic information, make decisions when presented with alternatives or perform exercises in logic. It stems from not knowing explicitly how humans do all of these things.

Perhaps we are straining too much with the question of whether machines can think or not. The picture comes to mind of those colorful races which were run in the early 1800's between horses and steam engines to see which was the faster.

Talking about the intellectual capabilities of men and of machines in the same breath is not out of order as long as things are kept in an unemotional perspective. Obviously there are similarities as well as differences in what man and computer do when they perform "thinking" tasks. But there is much to be gained by furthering our understanding of man's mental processes, and by improving machine calculating and even reasoning capabilities. We should not try to equate man and machine; rather we should try to augment man's ability through the agency of machines (and vice versa).

Let us review what we have learned about machines, particularly computers. Machines can answer telephoned questions, speak, take dictation, hear, see, and learn, translate, read, write, and design complex structures and systems—most of these are already in commercial use. Once these developments have been described more fully, an assessment of machine intelligence will be more meaningful.

For example, a manager can dial a series of numbers on his telephone. After a few seconds a voice will inform him, "Your order number 03007-4 for 30,000 sets of part number 3456-A was shipped February 17 via motor freight; thank you." The polite machine that answers in spoken English is an IBM 7770 audio response unit which contains a vocabulary of words and sounds stored on a magnetic drum. When an inquiry is made—by dialing a code number—an audio response to the inquiry is assembled automatically and transmitted back to the questioner through an ordinary telephone line. While the prerecorded vocabulary of the 1964 models of the machine is limited to slightly over a hundred words, it can report quickly and inexpensively on a billion characters when hooked up with a large computer. For example, a broker can get immediate replies to high and low stock quotations, number of shares traded, and latest market price on any listed stock.

In a separate development, scientists at Philco Corporation's Advanced Communication Techniques Laboratory have designed and built a machine that synthetically generates words. Through sound creating systems it is possible to duplicate anyone's voice. Theoretically at least, it is possible to synthesize Enrico Caruso's voice singing "I'm Dreaming of a White Christmas." For the time being, however, these dybological voices have a sound quality about that of a mechanical talking baby doll.

A further voice-related development is typewriting directly from the human (or otherwise) voice. The electronics department of Kyoto University in 1959 reported work on a device which prints in Roman letters whatever is said. In similar work, Stanford University's Adaline (acronym for adaptive linear neuron) can—in addition to reading electrocardiograms and predicting weather—type out simple spoken sentences. Also, personnel at the Bell Telephone Laboratories have developed a machine called Audrey (for automatic digit recognizer) which can "hear" and identify ten spoken numbers and sixteen of the 40 basic sounds of English. To indicate that the spoken digit or sound is understood, Audrey flashes the appropriate light on its (her?) display console.

There are pattern-recognizing machines that can identify handwritten or printed letters, geometric shapes and even pictures of people regardless of a wide variety in size and orientation. These "perceptive machines" are not computers in that they are not programmed to react in a predetermined way, but rather they are taught to identify visual and aural inputs. There are machines that can design aircraft, automobiles, bridges, roadways, and ships.

Another form of machine intelligence is translation from one language to another. As early as 1910, Popular Mechanics carried a short article describing the novel but undeveloped suggestion of a Michigan inventor—an interpreting telephone. If Chinese, for instance, was spoken into one telephone, a converting device attached to the receiving telephone would translate the incoming message to English by moving an indicator opposite the "Chinese" position. The possibility of actually doing this is considerably less remote today than in 1910.

Existing machine translators are relatively prosaic in their operation, even though they perform their task with speed, and work with large vocabularies. The Mark I, an experimental IBM machine, translates Russian into English at a rate of 1,800 words per minute (as compared to a human who averages 2,600 words a day). A glass disk the size of a long-playing record holds Mark I's vocabulary of about 600,000 Russian words. The disk is scanned by an electronic beam in the same way a human scans a dictionary. Of course, translations are essentially on a one-for-one relationship and the final outcome, while generally serviceable, often yields confusing or humorous results. For example, the English input: "The spirit is willing, but the flesh is weak," produces the Russian version —when retranslated—"The vodka is strong, but the meat is rotten." Another humorous classic is "out of sight; out of mind" translated into "blind idiot."

While admittedly having trouble with translations, commercially available machines have been able to read written and printed characters, error free, for quite some time. More interesting for our purpose are the letter/number character readers which perform their function in much the same way as humans. The National Cash Register Company has developed a machine optical reader with a capability of 11,000 characters per second or about 120,000 words per minute. In actual practice the reading rates are slower because of the difficulty of moving paper documents—cash register tapes for instance—at speeds permitting such fast reading.

IBM's 1418 optical character reader is the first to be linked directly into a computer system. The transistorized device reads—at 480 characters a second—printed business information from paper or card documents. It then automatically translates the data into machine language for direct entry into a computer. In this way, notices, coupons, bills, and other automatically printed forms are sent to customers, and on their return are fed directly into electronic accounting machines. Also in use is an optical reader which can handle hand-printed information such as found on department store sales slips.

Machines can read, but can they write? If there were any need for mechanized handwriters, I am sure they would be developed. What is more urgently required—beyond the punchtape-operated typewriter which types standardized sentences and paragraphs from coded inputs—is automatic typesetting machines and high speed printout devices. The problem with typesetting is not simply one of justification such that each line of type is of equal length and forms a straight right margin, but of hyphenation. As any typist or compositor knows, you should not split a word any place. There are rules and exceptions to these rules. Several companies offer computer-operated typesetting systems which take edited material that has been manually typed into paperpunched tape and convert this into justified lines, hyphenated words, and a new tape for insertion into a linecasting machine. The typecasting is performed at about 9,000 lines per hour.

In the area of printout equipment, Radiation Incorporated has developed an experimental model of a high-speed printer. Modern computers can assimilate and process vast amounts of data, but a bottleneck occurs at the output when information is transcribed on conventional printout machines, a letter or line at a time. Radiation Incorporated's new printer "types" letter/number information from a computer at more than 60,000 characters per second, or 30,000 lines of 120 characters each minute. By using dry electro-sensitive fixed-stylus recorders, the unit could print out the King James version of the Bible in a little over one minute.

So far we have talked about single-faceted machine capability: machines that synthesize sound, translate or distinguish shapes, and so on. Certainly some of these machines can be combined—and no doubt will be—to provide an extended complex function. To illustrate, in the near future we can anticipate a single machine that will optically read pages of foreign text, translate the information into English, as well as typeset and print the result in final form.

Not all new product developments are aimed at the immediate commercial market, as were the previously cited examples of machines which can speak, hear, read, translate, and design. Some products are more oriented toward the research area and aim at uncovering new knowledge and finding potential applications in the learning, decision making, and reasoning processes. To shed a little light on the dimly understood subjects of problem solving and other aspects of human intelligence, work which outwardly resembles game playing, is being performed in universities, research centers and companies.

It has long been known that games are convenient simulations of actual situations; there are games of war (chess), games of finance (Monopoly), games of territorial conquest (go), games of adventure (Parcheesi), and so on. Needless to say, some of these games call for great skill and intellect. The underlying nature of these complex human abilities, however, remains essentially hidden; a person can be a master at chess without knowing anything about decision theory, memory processes, and symbolic logic.

Experimentation in machine-game playing does not necessarily try to duplicate human problem-solving methods. However, when a general purpose digital computer is programmed to play games such as chess or checkers, the similarities and differences between biological intelligence and dybological intelligence can be objectively examined. Researchers in this area are careful not to fall into the "analogy trap" whereby every new computer discovery is immediately used as an explanation of human brain functioning. Researchers are careful to separate the simulation of intellectual results from duplication of the process whereby these results are achieved.

Chess seems to be the top rung in the ladder of intellectual games because of the numerous possibilities of offensive and defensive strategies. Thus it has attracted the attention of the developers of intelligent machines. Claude Shannon in 1949 pioneered the work in the simulation of intelligence through machines. He examined and discussed many of the basic problems that were encountered when developing a framework on which understanding of intelligence simulation could be built. The late English mathematician A. M. Turing took up the challenge in 1950 and hand simulated a chess-playing computer program, although of a relatively limited nature. In 1956, a group of scientists at Los Alamos programmed the MANIAC I to play a passable game of chess. Alexander Bernstein, an eminent chess player and programmer at IBM, has done the most advanced and sophisticated work in this area.

Physicist Arthur L. Samuel, at IBM's Yorktown Heights Laboratories, developed a checker-playing computer program. Starting about 1953, this work was done in Samuel's spare time in connection with his studies on self-learning machines.

Dr. Samuel chose checkers over chess as the game for his research because the simplicity of checker rules permits greater emphasis to be placed on learning techniques. There are 32 playing squares and five moves for checkers versus 64 playing squares and over thirty moves for chess. The computer program is provided with a set of routines which allows it to evaluate 28 game factors such as control of the center by kings, mobility of pieces, and so on. By winning or losing, the machine accumulates experience which then is applied when selecting future moves.

The computer "learns" to play checkers in the following way: The machine is first programmed to evaluate all possible combinations for a series of three moves from a given starting position. The machine moves ahead first, then alternates with the human partner. In doing this, the machine analyzes (scores) 125 different combinations of possible moves from a given arrangement of checker pieces and then picks the best move. Once an analysis is made, it is stored in the machine's memory and can be recalled in a fraction of a second when the machine finds itself in the same playing situation at a later game. In other words, a wise move once learned is retained for future use.

The machine's capability does not stop here. With a three-move-ahead strategy in its memory, the machine uses this as a reference point for analyzing three additional moves for a total of six moves ahead. Having reached this point the machine can then "see" the most advantageous plan of attack 20 moves ahead.

Dr. Samuel's checker-playing machine also has the ability to "unlearn." This flexible feature is as important for machine intelligence as it is for human intelligence. We know we cannot blindly and indefinitely build in a direction indicated by past successes; situations often arise which puncture our generalizations. Yet a happy balance must be found in which success adds to the strength of a generalization (reinforcement), while failure diminishes its strength (forgetting). Because success and failure do temper human judgment one way or another in a continuously variable fashion— as opposed to causing complete acceptance or rejection—duplicating this ability provides a large step forward toward simulating human intelligence in machines. Put another way, machines can distinguish between various shades of gray rather than being always forced to choose between white or black (as many lower forms of animals must do).

How does Samuel's checker-playing machine compare to a human? In the summer of 1962 a match was held with Robert Nealey, a former Connecticut checker champion, and one of the nation's foremost players. From the results of the match, the machine (an IBM 7090 computer was programmed) and Mr. Nealey were evenly matched. Regarding one of the games in which the machine won, Mr. Nealey is quoted as saying:

It is very interesting to me to note that the computer had to make several star moves in order to get the win, and that I had several opportunities to draw otherwise. This is why I kept the game going. The machine, therefore, played a perfect ending without one mis-step. In the matter of the end game, I have not had such competition from any human since 1954, when I lost my last game.

An interesting side light of Samuel's work was the disconcerting effect of the machine's swift and seemingly effortless playing style. It can locate all available moves from a given board position in 2.6-thousandths of a second. This gave the machine the same decided advantage that an emotionless professional poker player enjoys when playing with an emotion-revealing amateur. Cold-blooded or not, the machine politely prints out at the end of a winning match: "Sorry, you lose. Thanks for the game."

And what about the future game-playing ability of machines? In four years, Dr. Samuel's machine developed from an "average checkers player" to a "champion." In 1958, Mikhail Botvinnik of the Soviet Union (and the world's champion chess player at that time) said in Russia's Literary Gazette, "It seems to me that in the future the machines must excel the grand master. Then, evidently, there will be two championship tournaments; one for grand masters; one for machines." There is a teacher in Russia who, no doubt, has had a change of heart—as have many others. He wrote the following poem after being told that machines could play chess and even beat the then current Soviet world chess champion, Smyslov (who was later beaten by Botvinnik):

> It may say "check" and may say "mate"
> But it's just an automation;
> By it, I feel free to state
> Smyslov will not be beaten.

In the over-all area of "intelligent" machines, Alan Newell and J. Clifford Shaw of the RAND Corporation and Herbert A. Simon of the Carnegie Institute of Technology have done the broadest work. Daniel D. McCracken, a computer consultant at Ossining, New York, tells in DATAMATION Magazine of an incident that took place about 1959 at the RAND Corporation in California.* The incident related to work being done on RAND's high-speed problem-solving digital computer called the JOHNNIAC (named in honor of the late John von Neumann):

Cliff Shaw one morning called up Fred Gruenberger, who also works at RAND, and asked him to participate in a little game. Cliff explained the axioms of propositional calculus to Fred, who had had no previous contact with the subject. Cliff then gave Fred one of the first theorems and asked him to prove it. Fred sweated for nearly an hour, going down blind alleys, trying little "experiments," occasionally getting hints from Cliff. Finally, he found a proof.

At this point Cliff said, "Tell me, Fred, have you been thinking?" Fred's reply was that he sure thought he had, and as a matter of fact, he hadn't thought so hard for months as he had in the past hour. Cliff's response to this, in essence was, "That's very interesting because I have JOHN-NIAC's proof of the same theorem. It went down approximately the same blind alleys, generated pretty much the same hints as I gave you, and produced exactly the same proof.

As part of the work described in the above incident, Newell, Shaw and Simon developed a program to prove theorems in elementary symbolic logic, again using the JOHNNIAC. The group fed the machine axioms and rules of inference for the propositional calculus from *Principia Mathematica* by Whitehead and Russell. The machine was fed the first theorem which it successfully solved. The group fed in the second theorem and asked the machine for a proof, using the axioms and the first theorem. Proceeding in this way, the JOHNNIAC produced proofs for most of the theorems in the second chapter of *Principia Mathematica*. In one case, the computer found a proof that required fewer steps than the text solution.

* "A Progress Report on Machine Intelligence," DATAMATION, F. D. Thompson Publications, Inc., New York, September/October 1960, p. 12.

To show the rapid development in this field, Hao Wang from the University of Oxford set up a computer program (while doing summer work at IBM in 1958) which algorithmically proved all of the theorems in mathematical logic in Whitehead and Russell's book. In later work at Bell Telephone Laboratories, Wang enabled an IBM 704 computer to prove 350 of the Whitehead and Russell theorems in less than nine minutes.

Many opinions on the subject of machine intelligence have appeared in print. Few, if any, of the opinions are objective; the nature of the subject is such that it is not broached unless one has strong feelings about it one way or the other.

One of the more outspoken disbelievers of computer intelligence, Robert E. Slater, Vice President of John Hancock Mutual Life Insurance Company wrote in the Harvard School Bulletin in 1957:

... those machines are morons. Don't let anyone tell you they are giant brains or will replace the human mind. They can't because they're just plain stupid. You have to tell them every last thing to do, and every detailed step about how to do it.... Working with such feeble minded creatures demands special training because instructing them is tricky business.

Consider the following statement made in 1954 by the neurophysiologist John H. Troll:

The human memory is a filing system that has a far greater capacity than that of the largest thinking machine built. A mechanical brain that has as many tubes or relays as the human brain has nerve cells (some ten billion) would not fit into the Empire State Building, and would require the entire output of Niagara Falls to supply the power and the Niagara River to cool it. Moreover, such a computer could operate but a fraction of a second at a time before several thousand of its tubes would fail and have to be replaced.

Some take the opposite position: machines not only think, but probably will prove to be better at it than humans.

A German scientist, Professor Karl Steinbuch of the Technical University of Karlsruhe, states:

In my opinion the future computers will lead to achievements beyond the powers of human intelligence. It seems probable that the present generation will see a . . . technical achievement whose significance will be as great as that of atomic physics and space flight . . . the development of learning machines over their human counterparts will be evident for a wide range of mental (and not exclusively mathematical) activity within, at the latest, the next two or three decades, not only because of their speed and reliability but also because of their capacity for abstract formulation and freedom from prejudice.

The late Dr. Norbert Wiener, famed mathematician of Massachusetts Institute of Technology and "father" of cybernetics stated:

It is nonsense to assume that the machines man has made cannot outthink and perhaps outwit him.

Wiener also felt that machines can and do transcend some of the limitations of their designers; that while a machine may be less intelligent than the men who design them (for the present) a machine can outperform man—perhaps escape from the dominance of man—simply because of the machine's speed of operation. He advocated a flat rejection of the "assumption that machines cannot possess any degree of originality."

Blunt statements are difficult to refute because of their general nature. One person may say computers are stupid and the next may say they are already smarter than man. It is when they try to elaborate on their themes that many of the weaknesses of their arguments emerge.

For example, consider the second sentence of Slater's statement: "You have to tell them every last thing to do, and every detailed step about how to do it . . ."

At first glance, one is left with the feeling that any machine that has to be told in detail "what to do" is stupid indeed. But is there a limit to what a machine can be told to do? Storage and retrieval of knowledge is not a large problem. The Marquardt Corporation's Astro Division has a memory device which could record everything written in the last 10,000 years in a six-foot cube. There is no reason why machines cannot be devised with an inductive capability to think for themselves.

Others, who claim that machine intelligence—to the extent of duplicating a human's ability—is a myth, use arguments that are valid at the time they are made, but do not take into account the rapidly expanding technology.

When Troll expressed his opinion in 1954, the relatively large vacuum tube was the primary functional component used in computers. Using transistors, the same computer of ten-billion human-like parts would take only one floor of the Empire State Building. However, the current third generation of computers use integrated circuits which, to continue our analogy, would require only a small office of the Empire State Building. Carrying the miniaturization process a step further, current technology indicates component densities enabling 10-billion computer parts—which are essentially on-off switches—to be packaged in a drawer of a desk.

Regarding small packages, the field of cryogenics can yield even smaller packaging possibilities. Computer components, called cryotons, operate at ultra-low temperatures and consist basically of two metals that become superconductive and sensitive to magnetic fields at near absolute-zero temperatures. These cryotons can be deposited with the use of an electron microscope in lines less than the visible wavelength of light in width. In essence, this allows packaging billions of units in a cube that measures one-tenth of one inch. John von Neumann once calculated that electronic cells could be ten billion times more efficient than biological cells (they are already one million to ten million times faster in operation).

However, we must remember when playing number games, that complexity is also important. For example, neurophysiologists are beginning to realize that a brain cell does not represent a simple switch (as does a tube, relay, or transistor) but may provide a thousand or more equivalent functions in itself.

Aside from number traps, many people fall into semantic pitfalls by considering the thought process only in human terms, and consequently exclude machines from consideration, or at best bypass machine performance in this area as trivial exceptions. For example, IBM in an advertisement (*Time,* May 1, 1964) informs us that "Computers don't think. They simply compare and analyze facts much more swiftly and economically than was ever possible before."

Some affirmative arguments for machine intelligence are made for personal rather than academic reasons. For example, engineers and scientists want a more tolerant public atmosphere in which to work. Generally they prefer to treat machine capability as realistically and accurately as possible; they do not wish to mollify or placate the public. Still they do not want to work in a society that is antagonistic to their work. Technology has struggled each step of the way as it moved from the impersonal to the personal. Even the early mathematicians had to operate in secret societies because their work was tinged by the public with an eerie supernatural glow, and study of human anatomy by vivisection is indeed a recent development.

Most would scoff at the idea that present-day engineers and scientists have to work in an environment oppressed by the hostility of public opinion. Yet a survey taken several years ago of high school students brought forth a picture of the "scientist" as a somewhat fiendish person who stole brains (or had his mute hunchback assistant do it during a lightning and thunder-filled night) for some diabolical research project.

The previously mentioned A. M. Turing, in 1950, wrote a now classical article, "Computing Machinery and Intelligence," in which both sides of the machine intelligence argument were examined. To avoid the semantics problem involved in the meaning of "machine" and "think," Turing suggested a question and answer game. In this game an interrogator can communicate with a human and a machine through a teletype machine; the teletype being used to remove clues of voice, appearance, and so on. The interrogator is to decide from the answers to his questions which is the human and which is the machine. Turing reasoned that if after hours or days of "conversation" the questioner could not decide whether the party on the other end of the line was human or purely mechanical, then the questioner could hardly deny that he—or it—was capable of thinking. An electronic machine passing this test would certainly have to be regarded as intelligent.

Below is a portion of Turing's sample dialogue between the interrogator and the unknown man or machine respondent:

Q: Please write me a sonnet on the subject of the Forth Bridge.*

A: Count me out on this one. I never could write poetry.

Q: Add 34957 to 70764.

* Turing was referring here to the mile long steel cantilever railroad bridge erected (1882-90) in Scotland's Firth of Forth at Queensberry.

Q: I have K at my K1, and no other pieces. You have only K
at K6 and R at R1. It is your move. What do you play?

A: (Pause about 30 seconds and then give as answer) 105621.

Q: Do you play chess?

A: Yes.

Q: I have K at my K1, and no other pieces. You have only K
at K6 and R at R1. It is your move. What do you play?

A: (After a pause of 15 seconds) R-R8 mate.

Turing felt that the then (1950) newly developed "electronics
computer" or "digital computer" would give a good showing in his
imitation game. While this confidence in machine capability is
understandable today, it is to Turing's credit that he had such
foresight based on computers that were in existence for less than
five years. Today there are thousands of such man-computer con-
versations (although more business-like) which take place at air-
lines' reservation counters, stock-brokers and banks. While a human
could take over in the central office, the clerk at the ticket counter
would have no way of knowing this unless the human traits of
hesitancy, erratic typing, etc., could be noted on the electric typewriter from which he received the messages.

Since 1950 computers have demonstrated the ability to do creative work such as play writing and musical composition. The hypothetical man in Turing's experiment may not be able to write
poetry, but computers can; at least the RCA 301 "poet-computer"
has this capability. Let us play Turing's game seriously; which of
the following poems is the RCA computer's "Poem Serial Number
929?" Do not look at the footnotes until you have decided.

Poem A: nouns to nouns
        wan
        wan

        too nons two

        and
        and

        nuns two nuns

        w and d
        ering

in sin

g
ular untheknowndulous s

pring

Poem B: While dream flowed blindly
              on broken hopes
          Still space drained sickly
              o'er broken loves
          Your light driven slowly
              from furtive men
          No heavens slept.

Having used his imitation game to indicate what was meant by the terms "machine" and "think," Turing then proceeded to examine several of the more popular types of contrary views on the question "Can a machine think?" For example, he pointed out the theological objection that thinking is a function of man's immortal soul and that God has given an immortal soul to every man and woman, but not to an animal or a machine. Hence, the argument goes, no animal or machine can think.

Turing accepted no part of this argument, but he did answer it in theological terms. He pointed out that the argument would be more convincing if animals were classed with men, for there is a greater difference between man and machines than between man and other animals. Turing further pointed out that if a soul were required for thinking, how do Christians regard the Moslem view that women have no souls?

Arguments such as these can and do go on endlessly. While they may be interesting, they are rarely ever resolved. It is more probable, I believe (as did Turing) that it is wisest to stay closer to observable facts. In this connection we can return to the "creativity" of machines.

Poem A. "nouns to nouns," e.e. cummings, 50 POEMS, Grosset & Dunlap, 1939, p. 22.
Poem B. "Poem No. 929," RCA 301, taken from *Industrial Research Magazine*, "The Truth About Learning Machines," Dr. Richard K. Overton, October 1963, p. 36.

Douglas Ross and Harrison Morse of the Massachusetts Institute of Technology developed, by means of a computer, a series of robber-sheriff pantomime scripts over a two-month period. Three of these Western playlets were shown on October 26, 1960 to a nationwide television audience by the Columbia Broadcasting System.

The playlets were selected from about fifty scripts "authored" by a program called Saga II, on the MIT TX-O computer. The plot of each story started with the same sequence: A robber appeared outside of a shack, entered, wandered about the shack, and then put down a bag of stolen money in a corner. At this point, the computer started creating the remaining script on its own. While it had almost unlimited choice in specifying the action of each player, the computer followed certain rules and constraints. For example, when the sheriff was first introduced into the script, he always was outside the shack peering in through the window. The computer followed a kind of logic: when one man aimed his revolver he could hit and kill, nick and wound, or completely miss his adversary. The shooting efficiency was a function of how many drinks each character had from a bottle of alcohol prior to the shooting. But the sheriff could go to the bottle only after a battle. This, of course, gave him an advantage; the sheriff won in three out of four scripts.

The purpose of the "rules and constraints" was to show that intelligent behavior is "rule-obeying behavior." By having the computer obey the appropriate rules, it created acceptable scripts as though it were intelligent. The introduction of the "inebriation factor" caused the actor to not follow the rules closely. This demonstrated that breakdown in the rule-obeying behavior led to less intelligent behavior, i.e., drunkenness. The inebriation factor affected not only the accuracy of the shooting sequence but, more importantly, the script-writing process itself. Thus the actor in question appeared drunk by inconsistent and erratic behavior.

Assuming computers know what a man knows is a dangerous practice. A pharmaceutical company had a computer automatically generate trade names for medicines. The computer was programmed to "make up" authentic sounding names and print them out on a list. This was done because thousands of names were needed to match the fertile output of the chemists and biologists: no one person being able to provide the required number of names.

When completed, the computer-generated list was about to be sent out. However, a fortuitous review of the results brought many red-faced reactions. Some of the names were four-lettered Anglo-Saxon words that certainly would prove embarrassing if found on the company's bottles in a drugstore.

A second example of computer creativity is musical composition. In 1959, Hiller and Isaacson at the University of Illinois' School of Music instructed the ILLIAC computer to produce fragmentary scores and improvise music to a limited degree. One such composition, *Illiac Suite for String Quartet*, has been played over the networks and has received mixed reviews from the music critics. More recently, sound patterns have been computer composed and played on electronic instruments designed for that purpose. About the most charitable way the public has reacted to this type of "music" is to call it "different."

Of course, it is possible to have a computer compose original music that sounds as if Mozart, Beethoven, or any other master wrote it. Each composer has his set of rules by which he creates music. These rules are relatively easy to apply in a computer program. I imagine the reason such "cultured" music has not been composed is because there is no challenge in the task. But assuming a symphony was composed in this way, say in imitation of Beethoven, I am sure the critics would admit the music was "acceptable Beethoven" but they would be quick to add, triumphantly, that it wasn't comparable to Beethoven at his best. This sort of comment is heard almost daily when people begrudgingly admit computers are very clever at solving problems but they hastily add that computers are not as clever as Einstein would have been at the same task.

Creativity is demonstrated in a more prosaic field by the computer-aided design systems. These systems, to which we have already been introduced, produce detailed engineering designs and drawings for the structural beams and girders of skyscrapers, the truss members of bridges and so on. Interestingly, these designing machines are referred to as "Junior Engineers" (in that they do the work normally assigned to technical specialists). We have already witnessed the transference of the titles "typewriter" and "computer" from the person operating a machine to the machine itself. If the trend continues—and there is no reason why it should not—

a person visiting a "medical internist" will be referring to a diagnostic machine and not a physician.

So far we have examined machines which actually exist: machines which are already used in business, commercially, or in the arts. Because the various capabilities of these machines are open to anyone's study, it becomes a matter of personal opinion whether or not these capabilities are put in the classification of intelligence. But we do not have to end our discussion yet. We can examine some aspects of machine capability which, as far as I know, have not been seriously claimed, let alone seriously argued.

In the work being done on self-growing, self-reproducing, and self-sustaining machines, I am concerned not as much with artificial intelligence or thinking as with simulation of the emotional aspects of human behavior such as the exercise of free will, loving, hating, and ambition. This concern is not academic to me, but real. As long as machines can be programmed and, in general, are under the control of humans, there is little need to be overly prudent. However, in the machines that I feel can be constructed, or grown, there are both legal and moral considerations which must be faced. For example, we unfortunately know that an automobile can and does kill. We do not blame the automobile, but the person responsible for the incident. But what about machines that can knowingly kill of their own free will, not because of maliciousness (which is strictly a human trait) but because they must to protect themselves (that is, the machines), and assure the successful performance of the function for which they were built.

The intent here is to reopen the debate on whether machines can think; where "think" is used in some meaning higher than merely the ability to solve problems or even to be creative. There is no question in my mind that some day machines will be able to experience many of the emotions we feel (they can already sense everything physical that we can), mainly because they will have to react emotionally in order to perform high levels of complex functions.

Thinking certainly is not a simple or singular process as, for instance, breathing or blood circulation. It is multi-faceted. Certainly, exercising free will, loving, hating, and ambition are emotional aspects of thinking. Machines can make decisions; in fact, they are very good at it. They can decide whether your dime in a vending machine is good or not. Coin changing machines can spot a counterfeit bill faster and more accurately than can a human. The number of business decisions made by computers are growing each day at a rapid rate. But is decision-making the same as free will? Free will is primarily thought of as noble, while decision-making is usually considered to be cold and succinct. Yet when a person tries to objectively describe what is meant by free will, the description invariably comes out in terms of decision making.

One may point out, a machine does not have the free will essential for distinguishing right from wrong, or that it is capable of committing a crime. First of all, we have to show that a machine can commit a crime. Let's say a dollar bill changing machine is dishonest; that is, it is designed so that it willfully can short change a customer or give the customer counterfeit money. The machine has many ways to decide when or when not to cheat. For example, it can cheat every third customer, it can select the person to be cheated by consulting a table of random numbers, it can examine the customer and short change only kindly looking gray-haired old women, and so on.

Someone may question whether the machine realizes it is doing wrong when committing a crime and whether the machine feels sorry if it does. Certainly machines can have a built-in feature by which cheating is recorded so that the machine not only knows that it is cheating but also how frequently this occurs. As for feeling sorry, the machine could be made so that cheating would stop after a period of time proportional to some "remorseful" setting placed into an appropriate control. Further, the machine could be programmed so that it would stop cheating if there was a good chance it would be caught.

Love and hate are essentially biologically oriented functions; we love those who are closest to us and hate those who would do us harm. We could make the coin changing machine give a bonus to its inventor, to its service man, and perhaps to exceptionally good customers. On the other hand, the machine could be made (assuming it was legal to do so) to shoot someone who tried to cheat or rob it.

Another example of emotional thinking is ambition. We already have machines that accumulate money in a relatively complex way.

These machines are legal in Nevada and are called slot machines. They have been designed to entice adventuresome customers to "try their luck" and, as far as I know, have never failed to take in more money than they have paid out. Interestingly enough there is an adjustment on these slot machines which is set to establish the amount of "ambition" a particular slot machine shall have. Could not such an adjustment be made on even more complex machines?

Perhaps in the above discussion (which does have its tongue-in-cheek aspects) we have strayed from the point that machines can, or will in the reasonably near future, exhibit intelligent behavior of the highest order. The argument could be raised that any example of machine behavior, no matter how complex, would by definition merely show a purely mechanistic form of behavior as opposed to an organic type of behavior.

As philosophers have long pointed out, we as humans are conscious of ourselves and our environment; we not only love and hate, exhibit charity and greed, and indulge in other "human" behavioral forms, but we are conscious of doing so. It is this consciousness that causes a great many people to reject anything that is not human. But can we say that machines never will possess the characteristic of consciousness? Dean E. Wooldridge asks and does not hesitate to answer this question in his book, "Machinery of the Brain." (McGraw-Hill, New York, 1963.)

"It is now known that there is no essential difference between living and nonliving matter. Living matter either has, or has almost, been synthesized in the laboratory . . . it is no longer purely science fiction to speculate that one day man may be able to synthesize the chromosomic content of cell nuclei and, by providing a suitable growth environment, thereby 'build' living organisms of considerable complexity. Now," Dr. Wooldridge continues, "if the resulting animal is similar to a naturally created higher animal, will it be conscious? It would be hard to doubt that it will."

Finally Dr. Wooldridge asks, "What then if a creature of similar behavior and intelligence were to be fabricated from components of quite a different kind—with a nervous system and brain based on electronic computers instead of neurons, for example? Would it too possess consciousness and the subjective feelings that go along with it? For all we know today, surely this has to be considered to be a possibility. Is it possible that, somewhere among their wires and transistors, there already stirs the dim glimmering of the same kind of sense of awareness that has become, for man, his most personal and precious possession? Fantastic? Perhaps."

I am fully aware that to suggest that machines someday can possess the most personal of human qualities may sound facetious to some and disrespectful of the beliefs of others. But, I hasten to assure the reader that neither facetiousness nor disrespect is intended. Rather the intent is to show that the results of human thinking can be duplicated in a machine; but with the admission that the process by which these results are achieved may, of course, be somewhat different in a machine than they are in a human. Nevertheless, I wish to emphasize the point that there are increasing similarities in the mechanics of human and machine thinking.

Several years ago, a leading brain anatomist was shown an uncaptioned diagram, which he was asked to identify. He guessed the diagram represented the pattern of neuron cells in the part of the cortex concerned with vision. What the scientist was shown was the wiring circuit of a perception machine which is taught to recognize and identify alphabetic characters and geometric shapes. This "mistake" on the brain specialist's part points out the growing similarity in the physical configurations by which man and more advanced machines perform similar functions. In other words, the trend is for the similarities between man and machine both structurally and functionally to become greater rather than fewer.

For example, an automatic target-seeking torpedo goes through essentially the same process in tracking an enemy submarine as a hunter does when stalking and shooting a deer. But the organic material in the hunter's head certainly does not look like the electronics and mechanisms in the torpedo's guidance "head." Yet there are valid analogies. The nerves and wires which carry electrical signals to each "brain" are essentially alike both functionally and structurally; both "brains" have memory devices; both can determine such parameters as range, range rate, azimuth, and so forth. The individual components in each of these brains—human and machine—seem at first glance to be entirely different. Perhaps they are quite different now, but will they always be? Biological cells, neurons in this case, are made essentially of protoplasm and hydrocarbons. Cells are made the way they are because in the evolutionary development of life it was obviously the most likely and successful way. The comparable components in electronic equipment such as resistors, capacitors, and transistors are made essentially of metals and plastics. These materials are used because they provide the most efficient and economical way that engineers and scientists can devise. This is not an apology, for only these materials (as opposed to, say, flesh and blood) can withstand the temperature, altitude, and other environmental stresses to which current-day products are subjected. But manufactured products still have a long way to travel along their evolutionary path.

A side-by-side comparison of the inside of a cell and a dybloc again reveals many differences, yet there are many similarities. The differences are obvious, but not as startling as the similarities. Both have protective membranes which are outer sheaths to allow control of the flow of desirable and undesirable fluids. Both sense their own dysfunction (or malfunction) and remove themselves in the event of failure. Both have internal pressures which apply force against adjacent cells or dyblocs to maintain structural integrity. Future dyblocs are planned which will contain means to generate their own energy and which contain sets of "blueprints" for the complete machine in much the same way as cells contain genes and chromosomes.

There are many other similarities between biological cells and dyblocs, but there is no need to examine them all to realize that the trend is toward minimizing the nature and extent of the differences between living things and machines. Because of this trend we see ourselves being duplicated, bit by bit, in understandable and explainable steps. These advances in knowledge of what we are and how we operate cannot help but be reflected—in some cases, painfully—in our personal attitudes.

We have long adhered to the belief that we are special. No doubt we are. However, history and the unfolding truths of scientific discovery tend to put the "special" on a firmer basis than the metaphysical reason our mythology provided. Man is not the measure of all things; but certainly he is of significance. The universe does not rotate around the earth; but the universe and our place in it are not diminished. The heart is not the seat of our emotions; but it is an organ of high efficiency and enormous stamina. The brain does not operate outside of the physical laws of nature; but in function and structure, it is way beyond anything we can duplicate or even completely explain.

In summary, we do not have to apologize for biological facts when they are taken out of the supernatural realm and placed on a natural and artificially duplicatable basis.

Chapter Nine

The Machine Tomorrow

*I hold that man is in the right
who is most closely in league with
the future.*

—*Ibsen*

As we trace man's journey deeper into the dybosphere we are forced to navigate more by crystal ball than by scientific instrument. And there is little reason to make an already exciting trip unnecessarily spectacular by indulging in wild predictions of the science fiction or Sunday supplement type. Consequently, there will be no attempt to predict what life will be like in the year 2000. I have been so disappointed in the forecasting results of people more learned than I in their five year predictions that I would not presume to try even further. Instead, I will attempt, in the following chapter, to describe in broad terms how our present lives will be modified by machines that are already in existence or whose feasibility has already been established.

I do not hesitate to predict the type of machines that will be found in the future nor what they will do. (In fact this will be done shortly.) The hesitation stems from not knowing whether these machines will appear next year or in a thousand years. Or, to reverse the coin, history has shown that new machines are developed which come as a surprise to everyone but the inventor. Radio, radar, transistors, lasers, and nuclear energy, to mention a few, seemed to unexpectedly spring from nowhere.

The reason it is impossible—or at least difficult—to foretell accurately the time a new machine will appear is the element of uncertainty. Some machines are stumbled upon by accident, as was the case with radar. Other machines have been fully conceived but circumstances were not ripe for their development. This was the case with space satellites.

Another reason why prediction is difficult is the variety of forces that govern invention. Some forces tend to keep technological development in a straight line; electronic hardware seems to be of this type. Other forces tend to create a technological zig-zag path because of action and reaction; space power systems are an example of this type of erratic progress. For example, satellites and space vehicles variously are provided with electrical power by batteries, solar cells, fuel cells, nuclear reactors, thermionic converters, turbogenerators, and so forth. First one type of energy source is in favor, then another, as advantages and disadvantages change with new developments.

Then there are balancing tendencies which maintain some sort of equilibrium as machines develop and mature. Automobiles, for instance, become larger and more comfortable, but more difficult to park and maneuver. So they become smaller; but the driver and passengers are too cramped and the size increases.

And finally there are circular trends in which old designs reappear. The most recent space suits for the manned lunar landing use the flexible arm, shoulder, and knee joints of medieval armor. Even more surprising, the Dutch wooden shoe seems to be the ideal shape for the well dressed astronaut as he walks on the moon's surface.

What is the wisest scope to set for predicting machines of the future? Of course we can take whatever we already have and say that their counterparts, yet to be developed, will be bigger and better, faster and more comfortable, or smaller and more efficient. But we want to talk about true machines of the future; machines which do not as yet exist in any form. Two such machines that have been widely heralded and which, no doubt, will appear are the anti-gravity machine and the matter-transmitting machine.

An anti-gravity machine is one which essentially repeals the law of gravity. How this is to be accomplished is not yet known; a better understanding of gravity itself is required. Chances are, however, that just as like poles of a magnet repel each other (such that one bar magnet will "float" in the air when placed over a similar bar magnet with the same N and S poles opposing) so will a piece of special matter (whatever that is) be repelled by conventional matter such as the earth. In other words, scientists are searching for a new material that will be repulsed rather than attracted by ordinary material. Another possibility that scientists are considering is to develop a screen that will cut off gravitational forces (the nature of which is not clearly known).

The matter-transmitting machine will provide for the disassembly of a solid body (conceivably a human being) atom by atom, transmitting the "pieces" through space or over wires, and then reassembling the atoms at some remote location.

Another version of the matter-transmitting machine is one in which actual material is not sent but rather information about the material is sent. (This is what TV scanners, transmitters, and receivers do with pictures.) By sending information about each atom, such as the element it represents and its position with regard to other atoms, a machine at the receiving end could then draw equivalent atoms from a supply source and arrange them in the proper order. In fact, if the machine could reproduce one article in this fashion, it could also reproduce many—just as TV pictures can be displayed on as many monitors as desired.

Many electronic engineers who have been too busy with their current assignments to read the latest technical publications are unaware that they are in danger of being relegated to the second team. A new technology based on an invention by B. M. Horton in 1958 at the Army's Harry Diamond Laboratories seems to offer more than electronics. The technology is referred to broadly as "fluid systems." Of course, fluids—liquids or gas under pressure—have been incorporated into systems for a long time: hydraulic brake systems on automobiles, pneumatic brake systems on trains, jet engines. Still we are not speaking of the "brawny" systems which provide power but "brainy" systems which provide control or calculation.

One does not have to be an Einstein to understand this technology which threatens to break the monopoly of something as complex as electronics. It is precisely the simplicity of the device which evokes so much enthusiasm. The basic principle of fluid system technology was discovered in 1933 by Henri Coanda, a Romanian engineer living in Paris. An analogy of his discovery will illustrate its simplicity.

First consider a length of wet spaghetti hanging next to a wall.

If the free end of the spaghetti were pushed to the wall it would cling there. But then the slightest lifting pressure would cause the spaghetti to separate from the wall and hang straight down. If two parallel surfaces with a small hole in each were used, the spaghetti repeatedly could be poked free from one surface and put in contact with the other surface. This clinging-until-pushed-free action is the equivalent of an electronic bistable digital flip-flop amplifier or, more simply, the basic on-off switch of computer circuitry.

To change from analogy to actuality we have only to substitute a fine stream of some fluid for the spaghetti. In actual devices, a jet of liquid or gas called the power stream is directed into an enlarged V-shaped throat area. The power stream attaches itself to one of the walls by generating a low-pressure separation bubble between the power stream and the wall of one throat area. A slight pressure from a control jet applied at right angles to the power stream causes the low-pressure separation bubble to dissipate and the power stream to switch over and attach itself to the opposite wall of the throat simply by being blown there by the force of the control jet. Amplification and switchings are accomplished because the tiny control jets redirect or start and stop much larger flows of fluids. A missile control system has already been developed in which a tiny force generated by a sensing device in a gyroscope is amplified a million, billion times into a jet to guide the missile.

Fluid systems (also known as fluidics and pure fluid systems) have several advantages over their electronic counterparts. In some instances fluid-type sensors which measure angular rates, velocities, pressures, temperatures, acceleration, etc. are inherently more accurate and sensitive than those used in electrical systems. Fluid amplifiers are relatively simple and inexpensive to manufacture; the estimated mass produced cost is about 10 cents each. They have few, if any, moving parts and therefore are expected to be extremely rugged and reliable. In addition, these devices can operate at temperatures ranging from close to absolute zero to several thousand degrees Fahrenheit. Transistors on the other hand are very sensitive to temperature. Fluid systems are not vulnerable to nuclear radiation or interference by radio waves, as transistors often are; nor do they present spark hazards around highly explosive atmospheres as found in fuel tanks.

Although fluid systems have already been used for practical purposes—following the trend of shorter and shorter incubation periods in the laboratory—this new development is classified here as one of the machines of the future in spite of the $14 million market for 1964 and the anticipated $250 million market by 1970. One reason is that the full potential of fluid systems has yet to be determined. In addition, these devices mark a new type of machine which promises even greater potential than existing machines. Using the bionics term, we can call these "wet" machines to identify them from "dry" machines, of which electronic devices are the most advanced.

Falling into the "wet" classification is a recent development: muscle-like actuators. These devices are made of long fibers of glass, steel, preloaded nylon, or other relatively non-stretchable material running the length of an expandable rubber tube. Pumping the tube causes the center to balloon or bulge and, in turn, the ends of the dybological muscle tend to draw together. In this way huge contracting forces are exerted when relatively small internal pressures are applied. Even though the movement, or stroke, of the muscle is quite short, highly efficient motors could be built if, perhaps, a series of these devices were connected to a crankshaft as in an automobile engine.

An even more life-like muscle system has been developed by Doctor Aaron Katchalsky, President of the Israel Academy of Science. Working under a USAF Office of Aerospace Research grant, Doctor Katchalsky has built three small mechanico-chemical engines. Basically, the engine consists of a protein fiber of collogen which contracts quickly, reversibly, and without fatigue in the presence of a strong solution of lithium bromide. Some fibers can pull a thousand times their own weight. When the salt solution is displaced by water, the fiber expands to its original length. Therefore, by alternating between the salt solution and water (the flow is controlled by a valve system driven by the fiber) the machine performs. More important, this mechanical work is produced directly from the chemical solution without going through the heat cycle normally found in internal combustion or steam engines.

Still another example of "wet" machine comes from electrochemical nerve cell studies being headed by Physicist Robert A. Stewart of the Space General Corporation. The basis for the new electrochemical nerve model rests on observations made in the early 1900's: visible waves can be created when iron wire is immersed in nitric acid. These waves are similar to nerve impulses. While much work remains, and techniques now unavailable must be developed, Mr. Stewart envisions a computing machine eventually emerging from this activity which would dwarf any now known. Such a computer would have parts packaging densities on the order of ten billion to one trillion parts per cubic foot. This is as good as or better than the neuron density in the human brain.

Engineers and scientists are considering a new type of "wet" battery: animal-generated electricity. Some have humorously suggested using electric eels for batteries on long space flights: "You don't have to recharge this type of battery, just feed it. And when it goes dead, you can make a meal of it." Yet there is a serious note. New and efficient power sources are urgently needed for space applications. Certainly nature's method of generating electrical power is a possibility that should not be overlooked.

In this connection, technical investigation has revealed that eels can produce hundreds of watts of electrical power. While the individual electricity producing cells, called electroplaques, of eels (and 500 species of fish) have been identified, many of the finer points of animal power generation are not understood. But enough has been discovered to indicate that as far as electrical output per unit weight is concerned, electric eels "package" their batteries about 100 times more effectively than lead storage batteries (0.11 versus 0.001 watts per gram).

Machines of the future will certainly make use of the power generating ability of the type found in eels and fish once the underlying mechanisms of these simple life processes are understood.

Recently, experimental models of bacteriological fuel cells, referred to as "bug batteries," have been built. The operating principle of these power sources is based on the ability of bacteria to strip hydrocarbons (which they decay) without the direct participation of oxygen. In so doing, the bacteria form water and a certain amount of energy to power their own metabolism. External circuits could harness the energy generated by these microbial reactions.

Most sea water contains vast amounts of both the proper bacteria and the waste material on which they feed. Imagine the amount of power which could be generated by placing electrodes (and semipermeable membranes which are also required) in some bacteria and food-rich oceans. It is also speculated that these power-generating schemes could be used in conjunction with cleaning polluted rivers and streams.

To predict the ability of future machines is difficult. Therefore we can only speculate on how these machines will be put together and the processes by which they will operate. We can look into the physiology of machines.

It is reasonable to believe that machines of the future will be self-sustaining; they will be capable of self-growth, self-repair, and self-reproduction. In fact it is quite evident and I wonder why a widespread effort to develop such machines has not already taken place. Perhaps we stand in the same position as those on the threshold of electrification in the factory, home, and office. While machines and devices had been available to generate and transmit electrical power for some time prior to the appearance of widespread electrification, a single reason was needed for triggering the avalanche of uses that still engulf us today. That reason, of course, was Edison's light bulb. Perhaps there will be some space application for a self-sustaining device that will usher in the widespread development and use of these advanced machines.

In general, the need for machines which are able to "take care of themselves" is not difficult to visualize. Current space programs call for levels of performance and endurance not easily achievable by today's designs. To reach the required levels of reliability in current space vehicles, a large amount of equipment is necessary. In the event of the failure of certain equipment, there is a standby set available. But the practice of carrying along these duplicate or triplicate equipments strains an already critical space and weight situation. For this reason equipment which repairs itself is desirable.

Concurrently, there will be missions that call for equipment which has the capacity to change (increase or decrease) the amount of its functional output. For example, as a space vehicle travels further away from its home base, the sensitivity and amplifying ability of a radio transmitter should also increase, as opposed to containing some peak capability initially as is currently the case. This feature of an equipment to inherently increase or decrease its functional ability is one of self-growth and retrenchment.

In limited quarters it is desirable to have equipment with the inherent ability to change functions from a process control computer to a navigational computer, as the need arises. In this sense the equipment is self-adapting.

It is essential, in certain circumstances such as space travel or remote, unattended locations, that equipment perform all of the functions expected of it with little or no attention of a support nature other than initially providing it with its power and constituent spare parts to keep it in repair. This implies a self-sufficient equipment.

Again, we have the features of a self-sustaining machine: self-repair, self-growth, self-adapting and self-sufficiency. Obviously it would not be feasible to design and build a simple self-sustaining machine. Self-repair of an essentially mechanical product is not practical and perhaps not possible. Assuming each part of a tractor is replaceable, it would take the equivalent of a complicated automatic record changer device to remove a defective part and insert a new part. But the "equivalent of the record changer" would, in turn, need another "record changer" to repair it, and so on ad infinitum. In other words, self-repair of this type is self-defeating.

The type of equipment visualized as being self-sustaining is one that is primarily electronic in nature (or one which uses the pure fluid devices discussed earlier) and which would, for the time being at least, have some mechanical parts which would not be self-repairable. The basic replaceable element of these self-sustaining machines is a module of standardized shape which contains the circuitry necessary for the equipment's function. In time, it is possible that mechanical parts also can be made of these replaceable elements in much the same way as bone is made of cellular material. These "vital" elements which make up a self-sustaining machine are referred to as dyblocs (contraction of dybological block).

In tracing the evolution of machines earlier in the book, we noted that the functions they perform are becoming more and more life-like. Yet the manner in which these functions are produced are far from life-like; life-like in the sense of movement and general vitality. In spite of the precision in a computer or the visual presenting ability of a television receiver, these devices are essentially dead in the sense we are talking about. There is no "movement" if one does not consider the flow of electrons in the various circuits: a cuckoo clock has more vitality in its parts than does an electron microscope.

Thus, the next major "mutation" to be found in the evolutionary development of machines will be a marked increase in their internal "vitality." These future machines will not have their functional parts rigidly soldered into place as they are now. Rather, the parts will be mobile; they will be carried to locations where they are needed in a pulsating flow in much the same way biological cells are carried in the body's blood stream. When the machine's elemental parts are worn out, they will be eliminated in a like manner.

How is a machine made which will grow, repair, and reproduce itself? Before we answer the question in detail, a few objective observations are necessary. When we see a plant or animal grow, heal itself, or produce others of its kind, we generally feel these things occur independently within the living thing. We feel this way because we ourselves are inside nature's factory, rather than looking at these vital processes from some remote vantage point. For example, the average person does not "see" the plants and animals exchanging waste products such as carbon dioxide and oxygen. We are not outside the total environment in which these life-producing and life-sustaining cycles take place.

In other words, the vital processes of living things are not independent but interdependent; they take place within and as a result of the "system" of which they are a part. Similarly, it will be possible for a machine to utilize life-like processes, but only as part of some larger "system." In the final analysis, the overall system which produces and sustains natural life is the same system which will "produce" and "sustain" machines. The only difference will be that machines will draw on the various facets of the system to different degrees. Perhaps machines will draw more heavily on gravity and electromagnetic fields than sunlight and moisture. Yet, this is not certain. Today's satellites draw their energy from the sun, as do living plants. Maybe machines of the future will share natural environments in a more similar fashion. In any event, the differences will be of degree rather than of kind.

There are current-day devices which are capable of self-repair. For example, automobile tires and aircraft fuel tanks have the ability to reseal themselves in the event of a puncture. A similar principle is being developed for use in far-ranging space vehicles to reseal compartment walls penetrated by meteorites. Also, broken metallic wires have been "healed" through the forced directional growth of whiskers made of a tin-magnesium-aluminum alloy. In a few days, the whiskers can bridge a gap of about one twenty-fifth of an inch.

Electronic equipment, notably telephone and TV transmitting devices, employ self-repair to a limited degree. When a failure is sensed, a redundant unit available for the purpose is switched in the circuit. Currently designed satellites make use of a type of self-repair which is analogous to a cigarette vending machine. That is, spare electronic units are stacked as are packs of cigarettes. When an operational electronic unit fails, a "fresh" one drops into place just as a fresh package of cigarettes falls into position as the bottom pack is sold.

But this type of self-repair has its limitations. If the failure rate of one particular type of electronic unit is higher than the others, its stack of spares will soon become exhausted. This represents a failure of the complete system, even though there are probably many spares left in the remaining stacks.

To circumvent this rather inefficient way of using spare units, an equipment can be built so that the complete system does not fail until the last spare unit is exhausted. However, this presents a problem if different types of units are required to make the system operate. The problem can be solved, though, if each spare unit contains all of the different functional capabilities required. When a failed unit is replaced only the required functions in the spare need be used. To use biological terms, units in the spares state are undifferentiated. When they reach their operating positions, they become differentiated.

How is this done? Let us switch our working analogy from a cigarette vending machine to a bathtub full of water in which spare units are floating about aimlessly. Assume that only one working unit shaped like an old fashioned drain plug is required and that it is in the position normally occupied by the drain plug. Also assume that when the plug-shaped unit fails, it breaks into small pieces. Consequently, when the working unit fails, its pieces are washed down the drain by the flow of water and a new unit is forced into the vacant space. If, through a faucet turned on and off by a floating ball, the level of water were kept constant, it would be only a matter of time until all of the spare units were used. Of course new spares could be dumped in the tub and in this way the "system" could be kept operating indefinitely.

To make our analogy a little more complicated, assume that instead of one drain hole there are sixty drain holes on the bottom surface of the tub. Each hole represents a different function to be provided by the unit occupying the hole. The spare units would be capable of furnishing any of the sixty functions, but which of the sixty were provided depended upon which hole it occupied.

The conversion of an undifferentiated spare into a specific functional unit is relatively easy to accomplish. First the units would be made so that they fit into the hole only in one way. On one surface of the replaceable units, metal contacts are arranged in the same way as are the sixty-minute divisions of a clock's face. Each of these contacts is connected to a different function inside of the unit. The holes on the bottom of the tub are keyed so as to mate with one or more of the sixty contacts on the surface of the replaceable units.

To become a little more practical, the tub can be changed to a tank and a circulating pump provided to return the water that ran out of each hole every time a unit failed. Further, an opening can be provided at the top of the tank into which fresh spare units can be fed. A screen can be placed below the tank to trap the discarded units.

From there we can make the system even more complicated. For example, we can have several tanks connected in a way in which spare units could pass freely from one to another as the pump circulates them through the system. Each tank, containing hundreds or thousands of holes, or operating positions, can provide a complex specialized function. One tank, for instance, could serve as the computer or brain for the machine. Another tank could be used to test spare units as they floated by, discarding faulty units and allowing the sound units to circulate.

The water, or whatever fluid is used, can perform services other than merely circulating spare units and removing failed or worn units. The liquid can keep the internal workings of the system at a constant temperature; it can carry chemical signals from one part of the system to another; liquid can be provided with coagulants to seal any rupture which might occur in the tanks or interconnecting pipes; the liquid may contain chemicals to be used to power fuel cells within the dyblocs.*

To take a giant step forward we can make the tanks and piping out of the same kind of units (which also now become building blocks) that provided the various functions of our self-repairing machine. But to do this effectively, the machine can not be assembled in a conventional manner. It must be grown to some nominal size first and then be permitted to grow to its full size by itself. To do this, the spare units must be constructed in a rather special manner. Their shape is almost dictated by necessity: The units have to nest together into a solid. Square blocks can nest in this manner but a machine built of cubes would not be structurally sound because the rows of cubes would form surfaces that could easily be separated.

When we leave the cube with its six sides, there are few remaining regular solid forms which fit together in a solid mass. Yet, there is one shape which is ideal for the purpose: the fourteen-sided tetradecahedron. Six of its surfaces are squares and eight of its surfaces are hexagons. Nested together in a pyramid they look like this:

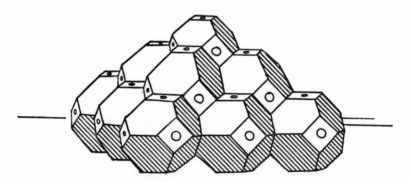

* The principle of the fuel cell was discovered over a century ago. A fuel cell works like a battery, to an extent, and offers nearly double the efficiency of the best steam turbine generator. The fuel cell can be made to weigh only one-twentieth of comparable high-energy batteries. In a dry cell or wet cell battery, electricity is produced through a chemical reaction. Eventually, the chemicals wear out, the battery "goes dead" and is discarded. A fuel cell is a battery into which fresh chemicals are fed. Thus, the reaction is continuous as long as fuel is available to feed the battery.

A column of tetradecahedrons looks like this:

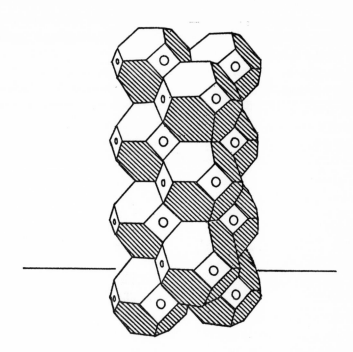

As mentioned earlier, these fourteen-sided, self-sustaining machine elements are called dybological building blocks or "dyblocs" for short.

When we try to develop the structual aspects of a self-sustaining machine, it is difficult to conceive any possibility other than the cellular construction of living things. Consequently, it is not surprising to see how fast our electronics packaging engineers are moving toward this basic-building-block goal even though the designers are not conscious of the direction. In fact, it is exactly this uncalculated development that leads me to believe that machines are on an evolutionary route of their own, even though it is human effort that provides the motivating force.

Current electronic packaging takes the form of modularization in which discrete components—resistors, capacitors or transistors and such—are encapsulated into plastic blocks. Protruding wire connections are then soldered to printed-circuit boards called, appropriately, mother-boards. Interconnecting these mother-boards are flexible ribbons of plastic containing multi-layered printed wires much like nerves are embedded in tissue. This current-day encapsulated electronic circuit is the precursor of the dybological cell or dybloc of the future.

But the dybloc is considerably more complicated than today's electronic modules; the dybloc will not only contain the electronic circuitry—which represents the nucleus—but the dybloc also will contain fuel-cells to generate its own electrical power. Additional circuitry and mechanisms will be contained in the dybloc to monitor its functional condition and trigger its removal in the event of wear or failure.

The dybloc will have many complex structural features. As presently conceived, it will have a "skeleton" in the shape of a jack (the kind that children play with). That is, the internal supporting structure will have six arms each at right angles to one another which meet at a point in the center of the dybloc. The arms, the axes of which pass through the center of the dybloc's six square surfaces, will be able to telescope like an automobile antenna. By means of the telescoping and a 45° rotation of each square surface, the dybloc essentially can collapse on itself into a relatively small cube. To allow this contraction, the eight hexagonal surfaces of the dybloc will be of thin, membrane-like plastic. A dybloc remains in this contracted state as it is circulated throughout the system as a spare unit. When a dybloc reaches the position requiring a fresh unit, its six arms expand outward, the square surfaces rotate 45°, and the dybloc assumes its characteristic tetradecahedral shape. Connections, both electrical and mechanical, are made at the square surfaces.

If a dybloc wears out or otherwise fails, its internal fault-sensing mechanism triggers a chain of events such as allowing valves to close, the dybloc to collapse, and locking devices to unlatch. The released dyblocs are carried through a sensing assembly, as are all other free dyblocs, and the failed one would be shunted off to a waste collection tank.

There are means to keep the stack of dyblocs above the failed one from being disconnected in the event of failure. This is done by arranging dyblocs in parallel. Mechanically, this provides for building solid walls of alternately interlocked dyblocs. Functionally operating dyblocs are arranged so that each has at least one surface exposed to a liquid stream (which is also true of body cells).

Suppose we wish to grow some identifiable configuration, say the letter "S" shown below. We start with a tank of liquid containing at least ten separate dyblocs randomly moving about. The liquid is agitated periodically causing the dyblocs to bump into one another. Each dybloc contains a one-volt battery to provide power for the various actions required.

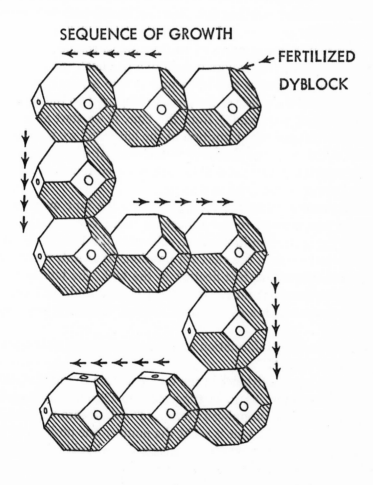

SEQUENCE OF GROWTH

FERTILIZED DYBLOCK

To provide a means of attracting and holding one dybloc to another, electromagnets are located in the four corners of each of a dybloc's six square surfaces. Also, each square surface contains a number of contacts to transmit power and signals from one dybloc to another. Inside each dybloc is an arrangement whereby power can be selectively applied to actuate the electromagnets on a square surface. For convenience we designate the six faces as top, bottom, left, right, front and rear.

The way in which a given set of electromagnets is energized so as to selectively attach one dybloc to another to form the letter "S" is through a coded punched hole tape confined in each dybloc. The punched holes are arranged to form the letter "S." The first or zero position is left unpunched so that unless something triggers them into action, the dyblocs remain in a free-floating state.

The punched tape is similar in principle to a player piano roll which contains the music of the piece to be played on the keyboard. As can be seen (or "read") from the tape, if we start at the first dybloc at the upper right position of the letter "S" we see that the second dybloc is attached to the right of the first dybloc. The third is also attached to the right of the second. The fourth is attached to the bottom of the third, and so on.

A mechanism inside the dybloc positions the tape over a set of contacts proportional to the voltage received: two volts puts the tape at the second position; three volts puts the tape at the third position and so on to the eleventh position. As already mentioned, when the dyblocs are free floating in the tank, the tape is at the zero position so that no electromagnet is energized. The tape retains its positions in a dybloc once it is set unless a special signal is received.

With the above information as background, we are now ready to "grow" the letter "S."

The ten or more dyblocs in the tank continue to move aimlessly about the tank waiting to be triggered into action. This triggering is accomplished by dropping a "fertilized" dybloc into the tank. To fertilize a dybloc, the tape is set at the number one position so that the left set of electromagnets are energized. It should be noted that left, right, top, etc., designations have meaning only to an outside observer when the letter "S" is upright. Also, these designations apply to a dybloc only after it becomes attached to some other dybloc.

There is a problem of communication between dyblocs which must be solved. A dybloc already part of the incomplete "S" has to convey to the next newly attached dybloc two bits of information: which way is "up" (or "left") and to which face the new

POSITION (or dyblock)	LEFT	RIGHT	TOP	BOTTOM
0				
1	0			
2	0			
3				0
4				0
5		0		
6		0		
7				0
8				0
9	0			
10	0			
11				

dybloc is attached. As there are 24 possible ways one dybloc can attach to another (six different square faces times four orientations of a single square face), 24 connection buttons are placed on each square face. By applying a voltage to one of these 24 connection buttons, the new dybloc—which has comparable connections—can "read" the orientation information and pass similar information along to the next dybloc.

The fertilized dybloc that has its electromagnets energized on its left side will attract some free moving dybloc as it tumbles about in the tank. Upon contact, the second dybloc will receive one volt

of energy through one of the 24 connector buttons. To this it adds
the one volt of its own battery (which is turned on by an internal
relay upon contact with the first dybloc). The two volts then move
the paper code tape to Position 2 which energizes the electromagnets in the left square face and a third dybloc is attached. This third
dybloc now has three volts which sets the tape at Position 3. Position 3, you will note from the tape code, calls for the electromagnets
on the bottom square face to be energized.

This process continues through the fourth, fifth, etc., dyblocs
until the eleventh dybloc is attached. The code on the eleventh
dybloc calls for no electromagnets to be energized so that the
letter "S" then is complete.

If desired, the dyblocs in the letter "S" could be freed by having
all tapes return to the "zero" position, including the one in the
fertilized dybloc. This could be accomplished by sending a chemical signal to the dyblocs which, when picked up by an electrical
device sensitive to the chemical, would deactivate all the electromagnets. The letter "S" would literally fall apart.

Assuming the code tape (desirably a magnetic rather than a
punched paper) was extended, say to include the entire alphabet,
"S" could be grown. Also, if there were enough dyblocs in the tank,
all other letters could be grown simultaneously by dropping appropriately fertilized dyblocs into the tank. For letters other than "S"
an initial voltage higher than one would be required in the fertilized
dybloc. For example, the letter "I" could occupy Positions 41
through 45 on the tape. The fertilized dybloc would then have its
code tape set at Position 41 and have a battery strength of 41 volts.

The letter growing described above uses only the left, right, top
and bottom dybloc surfaces. Consequently, the growth is in one
plane. By using codes for the front and back surfaces, three-dimensional solids could be grown. With a tank large enough and a supply of dyblocs great enough, a configuration of immense complexity
could be built.

To contain the mechanisms required to perform the actions described above, a dybloc would have to be quite large: about one
foot high. There is no doubt, however, that improved technology
will continually reduce the size of dyblocs, perhaps in time to microscopic level. (A typical radio circuit of World War II vintage

was reduced from approximately three cubic inches to less than two-hundred-thousandths of a cubic inch. In two decades, the volume has been reduced 600,000 times.)

With the exception of simple models, no dybological machines have been built; they are truly machines of the future. Extensive basic work must be done before building a working model.

We have talked of self-repairing and self-growing machines. Now we will turn to self-reproducing ones. Here we encounter the same type of semantic problems as we did with the word "thinking." The same is true with "reproduction." Reproduction conventionally is defined as the process by which animals and plants produce new individuals. If this definition is the only one accepted, then machines can not reproduce. If, however, we consider reproduction in terms of a result rather than a biological process then machines have reproduced themselves for quite some time.

Yet, we should not have to strain with analogy to prove that machines can reproduce themselves. We should establish a test for reproduction in the same way as Turing did for an intelligent machine. If the test is passed, then it can reasonably be said that machines can reproduce themselves.

Here is the test. We place a machine in a closed room with nothing else other than the things the machine needs to sustain itself (that is the equivalent of food, water, air, etc.). If after a period of time—not necessarily nine months—we go into the room and find a second machine similar to the first one, we can then say with reasonable certainty that the machine has reproduced itself.

Is this feasible today? I believe it is. The primary difficulty is to make a self-sustaining machine completely out of dyblocs. That is, the dyblocs must provide mechanical and structural functions as well as electrical ones. Dyblocs can be made to expand and contract along any one axis, or all three axes simultaneously, even though they are in an operating position. This ability is useful in that dyblocs can provide mechanical functions as well as those of an electrical or electronic nature. For example, the various pumps required to operate a self-sustaining machine can be built completely of dyblocs. This is accomplished by having the cylindrical portion of a tank-like vessel expand and contract in a concertina fashion. Input and output valves, also made of dyblocs, would be placed at one end of the cylinder to regulate the fluid flow.

Other "organs" can be fashioned in a similar manner. Further, the outer covering or "skin" of the machine can be formed from dyblocs which are forced outward in layers. The outermost layer would be "dead" dyblocs (in that they would not be in contact with a "life" providing liquid stream). This outer layer would keep sloughing-off with wear. Other anatomical problems can be solved with a reasonable amount of study and effort.

We have not yet shown how dybological machines, and more specifically, the dyblocs within them, can do everything required for self-reproduction. What guides or directs the actions and processes within the machine and its parts? In this regard, almost everything hinges on the dyblocs, just as higher forms of life depend on individual biological cells.

Any machine that can be built in the next several years, or even decades, could not produce dyblocs by itself as the body produces cells. Dyblocs would have to be made in factories just as other complex products are made today. Perhaps in time a dybological machine or a collection of machines could produce individual dyblocs from raw material unaided by any human effort. Or, the ability for a machine to produce its own dyblocs (as a body produces its own living cells) may never be required. We tend to think in terms of how living things evolved into complex forms, such as man. Because of this tendency we feel that machines have to follow the same path that living things have traveled. But this is not true. At a given point in time machines can pick up—assuming they are that far advanced—where man has left off. In other words, a robot-like dybological machine could build and operate factories just as man does. And further, there does not necessarily have to be only one "specie" of dybological robot. They can come in all sizes and shapes, as the need requires.

Self-reproduction implies that no outside intelligence is required to grow the object in question, a man or machine, to the point where it becomes a separate entity. The intelligence we are speaking of that is required to produce today's machines comes in the form of blueprints, specifications, punched tapes to direct numerically controlled machine tools, assembly instructions, factory routing instructions, and so on.

For a machine to "put itself together," each individual part or dybloc must contain a complete set of directions so that the final result is the complete "delivered" equipment. To achieve this, a complete set of directions recorded on punched or magnetic tape can be placed in each dybloc as we have seen in the example of growing the letter "S".

Some of the directions involve such things as informing the dybloc when to open or close certain valves in its six arms, when these arms should expand and contract and, in general, inform the dybloc how to react when certain signals are received. In effect, the directions tell the dybloc its station in life and how it is supposed to behave in given circumstances and in given situations.

Whether a machine is grown baby-fashion inside a "mother" machine, grown (after fertilization) in a self-contained enclosure as an egg, or grown in a conventional laboratory or factory is not of great concern: I am sure all three methods will be used. While the technology exists today to prove the ability of machine self-reproduction, the results would be considered by most as simply an unexciting stunt. Most early demonstrations of radically new developments are treated thus. Still, the potential of self-reproducing machines cannot be overlooked. Assuming machines are nurtured by man to the point of self-sufficiency, consider where the machines could go from there.

A complex dybological machine could be "intelligent" enough to knowingly alter the magnetic coding on the tapes of its offspring to produce a "better" machine. But the improvement processes need not stop there. True mutation and selection in a natural evolutionary sense is possible. A group of machines could be set aside for breeding and "improvement of the species." That is, a given goal could be selected beyond the capability of existing machines and by a trial and error process this goal could be met or at least approached. One obvious goal would be the performance of a given function with fewer number of dyblocs.

We (or the machines of the future) could randomly modify one of the codes on the genetic code tape of a parent machine. The offspring of this machine would then be a mutation. The offspring would be tested to determine if its "output" came closer to attaining the selected goal than did its parent-machine. If the score (for instance counting the number of dyblocs to achieve a given output) met or exceeded that of the parent, the offspring survives to become the new parent. If not, it is discarded (or its genetic tape returned to "normal") and a new offspring is generated. If a "pattern" of mutation were to be found (say finding which codes were most sensitive to beneficial modification) the evolutionary process could be speeded up. In this iterative way nonregressive evolution proceeds through successive generations until it appears that the maximum score has been reached.

Of course, in the process of this breeding, care must be exercised to assure that one set of characteristics is not so enhanced that there is a diminishing of many other sets of characteristics. For example, the number of dyblocs to perform a given function could be reduced to the point where there would be a structural weakness for some related function. Another related danger would be to "peak-out" at a score when, by making other alterations, an even higher score could be attained. To overcome this danger, the scores of other offspring more radically modified could be compared with the so-far attained best machine.

As is true in biological breeding, selection of the single best mutation to the exclusion of all others is a dangerous practice. Environments change as do needs. Consequently it is best to save the best few machines (or their genetic magnetic codes) at various points in time. These then could be used as the most likely machines to start producing new offspring at some future time when conditions have altered considerably. Further, a "second best" machine in one environment may be the best candidate for some modified environment at a later time or a different location.

A sort of sexual mating can be practiced in the evolution of dybological machines. That is, individual machines having desirable traits that have survived in separate evolutions can have their genetic codes "paired" to result in a new offspring. In this way the worthwhile trait is retained and at the same time the resulting offspring may be better in other respects. This practice need not be limited to two machines at a time. Many machines can be mated to produce a single offspring. In this practice, it is desirable to weight a given trait (which can be done by varying the magnetic strength of a genetic code) so that certain dybological characteristics are "dominant" and others "recessive."

Many variant possibilities become apparent. For example, the

best machines of several different generations can be mated; machines "designed" to perform different functions could be mated
to produce functions never before attained; highly specialized—but
otherwise inefficient—machines can be kept in the "stable" to be
used in unusual circumstances; or mutations of a predictable type
could be produced by having the "thinking" unit of one machine
superimposed on the "body" unit of another machine. The offspring of all these "possibilities" then could be mated and the
whole cycle repeated.

If indeed the above possibilities of machine development and
enhancement is probable—which I do believe—who then can say
what limit of capability is beyond the attainment of machines.

Engineers have always taken pride in the "efficiency" designed
into their product. However, this efficiency relates more to function
than to structure. An electric motor may operate at 95 per cent
efficiency but when it is discarded at "wear-out" 99 per cent of the
parts are still "as good as new." In other words, current products
are not as completely consumed structurally as were products of
a hundred years ago. A good pair of shoes usually was not thrown
away until seven pairs of laces, four sets of heels, three pairs of soles
and at least one change of uppers were made. Conversely, today an
automobile is often traded in when the nap on the floor rug is
worn.

Although we are an affluent society, the luxury of consuming only
a fraction of a product before disposal is contrary to the basic laws
of survival in a competitive situation. Dybological machines need
not be thrown away when they become obsolete or have otherwise
outlived their usefulness; the protective covering of these machines
can be dissolved and the remaining working elements "fed" into
new machines.

What is required to develop the machines of the future we have
described here? No doubt a realignment in our thinking on complexity is required. Currently, a product of several hundred thousand parts as in a guided missile or computer is considered awe-
somely complex. Yet, while machines of the future will require
parts numbered in the millions or even billions, this large number
of parts does not necessarily imply greater complexity. Paradoxically, machines of the future may be less complex if the different

kinds of parts rather than the number of parts used in their construction are a primary consideration. In this sense, a garden wall of 10,000 bricks is less complex than a birdhouse of 50 parts.

New disciplines will have to be formulated and current fields of effort expanded and integrated before dybological machines can be developed. Specialists in the design of future machines no doubt will need a much broader training than is currently required. The machine designer of tomorrow will be versed not only in the engineering sciences but also in the life sciences. Most likely, equipment will be designed by highly trained teams, each member having his own specialty. No one individual could be expected to be well versed in all of the essential disciplines.

After the initial prerequisites are met, designing machines of the future will require successive periods for improvement and refinement. The most marked requirement will be one of standardization. The functional output of these machines will continue to increase, both in degree and kind. But, as mentioned previously, the basic building blocks from which they will be constituted shall tend toward less, rather than greater, differentiation. One reason for this is the sheer number of dyblocs required. Another reason is based on the evolutionary principle that only the best dybloc designs will survive.

Economy is another reason for standardizing the basic building blocks of our future machines. When dealing with billions or trillions of parts (the human body has 100-trillion), mass production is the only practical solution. Also, as mentioned previously, it is desirable to conserve the parts from obsolete or otherwise discarded equipment.

How interesting it would be to speculate about the personal and social behavior of dybological machines. To cite one example, if two such machines were in an isolated situation with no fresh supply of dyblocs available, would the stronger machine overpower the weaker one to get at its dyblocs? It is an ominous fact that even today we speak of, and indulge in, cannibalization of old automobiles for their parts.

PART IV
LIFE
IN THE DYBOSPHERE

Chapter Ten

The Social Sphere

*Not so easily does a people lib-
erate itself from its social past.
Many ideas, customs, intoler-
ances, and tolerances, too, cling
on unperceived by those who
think that they live in days when
all things are new.*
—Hewlett Johnson

What will life be like in a world of mechanized men and humanized machines? It is self-evident that technological advances have
allowed man to conquer and harness the natural forces around him;
but has man conquered himself? When man enters the dybosphere
is he entering a golden age or is he, unknowingly, leaving one?
There are no explicit answers. But the relevant facts can be examined and the implications of the questions discussed. Hopefully,
we will then better understand man's place in the dybosphere.

What follows is more descriptive rather than prescriptive. There
are no panaceas. I believe that the forces behind man's changing
existence are too powerful to be altered. This is not intended as a
defeatist attitude, but as a realistic one. I do not fear the future,
nor am I alarmed at a mechanistic rather than a naturalistic existence. Certainly there is room for improvement in the way we relate
to our environment and to one another. And as a consequence of
our technology—rather than in spite of it—improvement is possible
and probable.

The above does not deny that cultural upheaval and misalignment will take place for signals of social convulsion are already
evident. Many culturally deprived and mentally subnormal youths
are reacting to their lack of a useful place in society. They resort to
violence in the streets and in the home to express their frustration.
In the predominantly agricultural society of yesterday there was
always the opportunity to work, even if it was on land owned by

189

someone else. Even the mentally retarded could perform useful tasks on a farm.

In today's advanced industrial society the situation has changed. Aside from the raw displacement of workers by automation, there is an increase in the required mental ability and physical coordination for success at a job. Many cannot meet the educational requirements needed in a modern factory. Thus these "unwanted" too frequently react violently against the society which has denied them the means for attaining self-respect and dignity, let alone a chance to secure a livelihood.

We are not considering a mere six or seven per cent of the population. The major portion of the problem stems from the relentless raising of intelligence levels required to satisfy increasingly sophisticated technological demands. Historically, the average schooling required in industry and business has risen from grammar school, to high school and, currently, two years of college as a general minimum. There is no reason to doubt that this trend will continue to the point where only a person with a doctorate degree will have the qualifications to "handle" a technical position. (It being understood that technical tasks, requiring less than this level of training, will be performed by machines.) Here, in essence, we can see the emergence of a new elite group.

But what of the remaining 95 per cent who are not intellectually equipped to join this inner circle of new technological leaders? It is important to remember that all tasks will not be of a technical nature nor are all tasks best performed by machines, at least from the sociological point of view.

To illustrate, there are many mechanical aids in the beauty parlor. No doubt the whole process could be mechanized. But women still want "personal" attention. (Neighborhood gossip, among other things, is difficult to mechanize.) The price paid for this type of human service may seem exorbitant compared to previous standards. Yet the cost could be ten times higher, and still make economic sense. The situation is actually a means of distributing the wealth created by the greater productivity of machines (brought about by those in the "upper" five per cent of the intelligence scale) among those people in the "lower" 95 per cent.

While everyone may not be capable of absorbing knowledge at advanced collegiate levels, the efficiency and effectiveness of our educational process can be improved on all levels. While some of the improvement will stem from advances made in conventional teaching methods, the greatest academic gains will be made through the use of mechanical teaching aids. (Again it is not a case of man *or* machine but man *and* machine—machines being used to solve the problems they create.) Mechanical teaching aids are not new; they've probably been used since antiquity. More recent examples of the use of machines in teaching are the visual aids: movies, slide projectors, and TV. Additionally, machines are used to ease the administrative load of our academic institutions. For example, thousands of students are registered and their classes scheduled in an hour's time through the use of a computer. The machine's high-speed printer provides lists of students in each class. Schedule changes and course realignments can also be made by the computer.

Regarding the computer, there is a growing trend to teach high school students the use of computers to solve problems: conventional arithmetic as well as advanced mathematical problems of calculus, number theory, algebra, and analytical geometry. The college-bound student with some computer training enjoys an advantage when he arrives on campus and a college without one or more computers for student use is becoming a rarity.

At the other end of the student scale, the kindergarten youngster is making use of computerized teaching aids. The Edison Responsive Environment System, developed by the Thomas Alva Edison Research Laboratory, looks something like a piano with a typewriter keyboard. When the child strikes one of the keys, the machine speaks the letter and displays it in large type on a roll of paper in front of the tot. After the young student has had some fun experimenting with the machine, the machine takes charge; in a friendly, patient voice it instructs the child to hit a particular key, say an "R." All the letters other than the "R" are locked. By trial and error (chances are the child doesn't know an "R" from any other letter) the child finds the right key. Using this method, youngsters learn to read about one third faster than those taught by skilled teachers using conventional methods.

Already in common use along with tape recordings and language laboratories is the teaching machine, developed by Professor B. F. Skinner of Harvard University. The teaching machine is a simple mechanical device which presents information and questions to a student. Programmed material printed on a roll is displayed in one of three rectangular windows. The student reads the information and in a second window writes the answer to a question. He then turns a knob which reveals the correct answer in a third panel. If his answer is identical with that of the answer panel, he pulls a lever and goes on to the next item. If his response differs, he pulls another lever so that when he has completed the lesson, the machine will return to the question incorrectly answered.

The basic principles underlying teaching machines explain their success. The material to be presented is absolutely clear and simple. The student receives immediate reinforcement or reward, as opposed to having to wait until the teacher corrects his paper. The information presented by the machine gradually grows in complexity, but the pupil's assimilation of factual material is tested item by item as he goes along. Bright students can romp through a program swiftly and move on to new ones, less intelligent students can take longer.

From an early start almost a decade ago, teaching machines have grown in complexity in some cases, and have been simplified to textbook size in others. Teaching machines that utilize computer storage memories which contain facts numbered in the millions are under development. They contain programs and routines permitting a "conversational" approach between machine and student. Concurrently under examination are the psychological principles of teaching and learning. Some of the original concepts in this field are being modified or even reversed in light of new findings. For example, although earlier machines presented portions of information effectively, the student tended to lose sight of the major thought being presented. The situation is similar to examining very carefully each bit of stone in a mosaic picture but never standing back to view the picture as a whole. This deficiency has been remedied.

Despite the fact that teaching machines have proven successful, many are repelled by the idea of mechanizing the schools. They state that the classroom is being converted into an aseptic assembly line of learning complete with pushbuttons. Even though the machines are admittedly more efficient than human beings, the objectors point out that an immense and crucial area of education is being sidetracked; the area dealing with values, feelings, and convictions they say can hardly be programmed on a machine. Also, because there is only one "right" answer, the critics point out the danger that the students themselves will think mechanically. Machines can show students how to punctuate and how to avoid grammatical errors, but they cannot teach them how to think through an idea or how to express themselves with impact and grace.

The proponents of teaching machines point out, on the other hand, that for every gifted teacher capable of inspiring and enlightening students, there are many more mediocre teachers who cannot do this, and in fact are far less effective than machines. Machine proponents also point out that even the best of teachers can only present their own limited skills, while a machine program embodies the sophisticated efforts of many specialists.

How are these divergent views to be reconciled? To repeat, it is not a case of either man *or* machine, but of man *and* machine. There is no need to settle for an all black or all white solution; there are many happy shades of gray. Factual material as found in mathematics, languages, history, spelling can be presented by programmed instruction. The significance, deeper meaning, and interest provoking application of these facts can then be presented by teachers freed from the many mechanical chores they previously faced; chores which are better handled by a machine.

In this connection, it is interesting to note that the evolutionary development and implementation of teaching machines are following rigidly the timetable set by current academic needs. The delaying tactics of the enemies of change do not seem to slow the process, nor does the impetuosity of the new radicals seem to accelerate it. The use of teaching machines is only one representative example of the many ways in which modern youth are being groomed to take their places in our mechanically-oriented society.

Primitive man had his plain or jungle, agricultural man had his farm, and current-day man has his city; cave-dweller, farm-dweller, city-dweller. This I believe represents the three epochs of total human history. Perhaps there may be a fourth, or more, but I cannot conceive of any. Cities may be completely roofed, built underground or in the oceans, but they still will remain cities.

Centuries ago (even millennia) there were metropolises with large populations, but each was different. A world traveler of the time could tell one city from another by its distinctive architecture, from the people's dress, the mode of transportation, or from the culture. Today he must look for the other part of the name on the Hilton Hotel to identify the city. Even the Eastern cities, such as Bombay and Tokyo, are rapidly losing their native characteristic forms and exotic manner. Not only are the automobiles becoming more alike in the cities of the world but also the road signs, gas stations, and cloverleaf interchanges.

Just as machines are being standardized, so are the cities of the world with their highly similar supermarkets, subways, and hamburger stands. And further, the same mechanistic forces molding the cities are also molding the inhabitants of these cities into highly similar patterns of social and cultural behavior; urban life is becoming the same regardless of the city's location on the globe.

Another indicator of the crossover point where man left the biosphere and entered into the dybosphere is the time when more people lived in the city than in rural areas. Starting about 1900, the rural population of the United States leveled off to a constant 55 million. The urban population, on the other hand, rose sharply from a stable 5 million in 1850 to about 125 million in 1965. The crossover point from predominately rural to predominately urban living occurred around mid-1952. (While the figures for the United States are treated as being representative of Western civilization, we must admit there is quite a variation even among Western countries. For example, in 1950, Scotland had more than four-fifths of its population in cities while Switzerland had only about two-fifths of its people urbanized at the time.) Contrary to popular opinion, the city of today can be made to provide the same high social and civic standards which the cities of antiquity offered the illiterate and unskilled who tended to flock there.

The future of the city depends upon cultural standardization: an inevitable process when diverse people are in daily contact. The current onrush to the urban areas of diverse ethnic and racial groups does create fear and mistrust among the populace. But in time, and with effective communication and healthy economic growth, the differences and ills generated by intermixing will disappear. Young people in particular, accept the varied cultures of others.

Perhaps not as obvious a problem are the requirements for integrating city-dweller and machine. The problem is clearly demonstrated by the flood of intracity traffic: the man going to work; the woman going shopping; the child going to school. The mixing of human and machine creates problems and stresses of its own. Providing more space for vehicular traffic is not an economically feasible solution. For example, the City of Los Angeles has catered to the voracious appetite of the automobile to the extent of giving up 70 per cent of its urban space for highways, roads and parking. Yet there are still countless delays due to choked traffic.

To find a solution to this problem, the State of California has issued study contracts to its aerospace industries. These studies are aimed at the development of the optimal transportation network for its citizens. Other sociological and economic problems to be solved by corporate engineers deal with methods to treat the increasing number of mentally ill people, the organization of information systems to gather, process, store and retrieve governmental data, and a program to minimize pollution of land, air and water.

Also significant is the increasing use of computers to aid in the administration of urban operations and in the protection of the city's citizens. To illustrate, police departments are turning to the computer for tasks more sophisticated than keeping track of parking tickets. The number of crimes committed each day in a large city is so high that detectives cannot assimilate all of the information required to pinpoint suspects. With the aid of computers, however, vast amounts of information can be recorded and retrieved rapidly such as a description of the weapon and type of getaway car, as well as threatening language, *modus operandi* and physical characteristics of the criminal. Following their use in business and industry, computers are programmed to provide answers when queried (through a teletypewriter) in normal English. That is, police officers can "talk" directly to the machine without converting their questions into elaborate code. Also, through the use of time-sharing techniques, many suburbs simultaneously make use of a centralized computer.

Already demonstrating its efficiency and speed is Operation Corral (for computer-oriented retrieval of auto-larcenist) in New York City. This method of spotting stolen and uninsured cars and those scofflaws for whom warrants have been issued involves a rather simple setup. As traffic passes a police car, individual license plate numbers are relayed by radio to a computer. The numbers are fed into the computer which then compares them with the approximately 200-thousand "wanted" lawbreakers. In less than one-tenth of one second the computer completes its search. If a culprit is identified, a second policeman stationed about a block down the street nabs the traffic offender. In the San Francisco Bay area a somewhat similar arrangement is used. A policeman phones the license number of an automobile he is about to stop for a violation. A computer scans its memory and tells the officer whether he has a wanted criminal or just an ordinary traffic offender. Police in New York State are considering a system in which closed-circuit TV cameras constantly read licenses at toll gates and other stopping places.

Of course not all the uses to which computers are put are so grim. They are being employed effectively in that eternal process of selecting a mate. In rural areas the problem of matching boy with girl is relatively simple. Social, economic, and religious backgrounds are invariably similar. Further, there is ample opportunity to meet eligible marriage partners at picnics, church gatherings and county fairs. While boy still meets and marries girl in the city, the matches do not seem to be as binding. The blame for a one-in-three divorce rate in the United States can be placed to a large degree on urban life.

Again, the computer is called upon to brighten a dim situation. Eligible men and women are matched with the aid of electronic data processing machines. While the romantic heart may shudder at the prospect of mechanistic mate matching, the chances for a lifetime of contented domesticity are claimed to be about 30 times higher than when nonmechanized methods are used. Once an eligible male or female fills out questionnaires detailing the basic factors of intellectual level, religious and emotional characteristics, moral values, desired goals, and personality traits, this information is fed into a computer. The machine then digests and evaluates these factors and provides the names and addresses of possible mates with matching tastes, temperament, and background. Once introduced, conventional dating and courtship take place.

To an increasing extent, machines are providing city cultures with the knowledgeable means to improve man's lot. Potentially, city life can be more rewarding and pleasant than rural life. This will be realized when machine aids are understood and properly assimilated for the enhancement of meaningful values and essential ways of urban life.

The word that characterized man's place in the biosphere was "exertion." The word that characterizes his place in the dybosphere is "leisure." Man once had to exert himself physically to strain, pull and labor in order to survive; now he does not. The machine to an ever-increasing degree takes over the work-portion of man's daily life. Another crossover point at which man left the biosphere and entered the dybosphere can be marked by the division of his sixteen waking hours. Historically, man spent all of his waking hours in toil, to feed and clothe himself and family. A hundred years ago, the average work week in the United States was almost 70 hours. But as tools were further developed, and then machine tools, the amount of his free time increased. By 1900, the average work-week was 60 hours and there were 36 hours weekly of leisure time, excluding Sunday. Free time finally exceeded working time for the average person in the late 1950's. In 1965 there were 40 hours spent at work and 56 hours weekly leisure time, again excluding Sunday. By 1975 it is estimated that 37 hours will be spent at work each week and 59 hours at leisure. Because of this "excess" of free time, the subject of leisure is getting intensive coverage in the press and other informational media.

Now that the age-of-leisure has overtaken the age-of-work, how do we describe leisure? The meaning of the term is not as apparent as is the meaning of "work." For example, leisure does not necessarily require the absence of effort, as seen in the man who comes to "work" exhausted on Monday morning and says: "Thank heaven I have five days in which to recuperate for next weekend." In this sense, one can say that man has been a "worker" in the past and he will continue to be one in the future. However, he will work less at an occupation and engage more in pursuits which we call hobbies. This is not a new concept; today we think of hunting and fishing as a form of recreation, but in earlier times these pursuits were primarily work.

Perhaps leisure is explained better as an attitude than an activity. When the late Sir Winston Churchill was building a brick wall in his garden he was enjoying a task of leisure. A mason, on the other hand, performing the same task under contract would be working to earn his living. Put simply, one man's leisure can be another man's toil.

We are reminded that man has struggled from time immemorial for leisure—now that he has it he doesn't know what to do with it. Actually, the problem of extended leisure is only a transitional one which even today is being solved. Unquestionably, we will devote the same intensive attention to spending free time as we once did tilling the soil. And it is not only free time we are spending. In 1964 more than $40 billion was used for recreation alone. Indoor and outdoor recreational activity is taking more than one-tenth of our income. Baseball attendance is 30 million annually and race track attendance is double this amount. One-eighth of the continental United States is used for recreational purposes with vacation travel consuming $10 billion. We spend $100 million annually on fishing and hunting licenses and $1 billion on our gardens.

There is an increasing trend for companies to provide "after-hours" recreation for employees and their families. Besides the traditional company Christmas party and annual picnic, there are bowling leagues, bridge tournaments, and evening art classes. Companies not only organize recreational activity but also provide the facilities to make this possible: tennis courts, ball fields, vacation retreats, swimming pools, bowling alleys, and country clubs.

Our taste for participative recreation is outgrowing the traditional hunting trip and golfing. In fact waterskiing—a stuntman's vocation a generation ago—now attracts as many participants (6 million in 1964) as golfing. Other popular sports borrowed from the stuntman are parachuting, parakiting (soaring in the air while supported by a large kite), and iceboating at 90 miles per hour. Psychologically, many feel the need to duplicate the excitement and aggressive outlets that the man of antiquity had when he encountered a saber-toothed tiger with only a pointed stick. The more sedentary among us are content to sit and watch television programs for endless hours (specifically, 300 billion person-hours in 1963).

Spare time will continue to grow, as will our capacity to find new ways to fill this time with pleasurable activity. In other words, we will spend more time traveling, camping, and attending adult educational classes where we can learn to paint, to play a musical instrument, or to knit.

Yet all free time is not devoted to play or hobbies. As my fellow engineers in Los Angeles can tell you, 10 hours per week are spent traveling (to and from work), five hours per week doing repair jobs around the house, and two hours each week helping with the household chores. Actually, if such things as attending evening classes to keep abreast of latest technical developments, and completing office work at home are considered, most of my colleagues put in the same 12-hour days as their great-grandfathers. Other professional and executive people do the same.

But we are losing sight of the trend; at least the trend for the vast majority of workers. There will always be people who cannot find enough hours in the day to do the work they have planned. Generally, these hard working/hard playing people are decreasing in number. The average worker now finds himself with more free time; there are more paid holidays, longer vacations, earlier retirement and so forth. A 35-hour work week is a reality for some and will soon become an actuality for others. You will find a great deal of time is wasted at work, especially when scheduled working hours are not strictly observed.

The major problem of leisure is not necessarily one of finding ways to profitably and joyfully spend free time. Rather, the problem is one of adjustment of an essentially "workless" (in the traditional sense of the word) world. Our social and religious structure is founded on the ethics of hard work and the avoidance of frivolous pastimes. Some feel that "idle hands are the Devil's workshop." How can we enjoy being unproductive when we are guilt-ridden with the prospect? Obviously, our cultural standards will have to change if we are to keep from becoming a nation of neurotics. There simply will not be enough "work"—with the new trends leaning toward automation.

One should not feel that spare time must be devoted to cultural pursuits or active participation in sports. There are people who simply like to play bingo or poker or sit around in their undershirts drinking beer. And they should be allowed to spend their time this way without the feeling of guilt or anxiety. Actually they are not miserable. It is only the professional moralists who feel that these "time wasting" activities must surely lead to a feeling of inferiority and dereliction.

Even though we now boast 1,200 symphony orchestras in the country where there were only 10 at the turn of the century (people bought more records of *Beethoven's Ninth Symphony* in 1954 than in 1934), it is obvious that only a small portion of the population attend plays or lectures. Most people prefer puttering around the house and garden or visiting friends and relatives.

Will purposeless leisure lead to a vegetative existence? Probably. Yet, leisure of the sitting-around-doing-nothing variety will not be the cause of mental and physical decay, but the *symptom*. In the past, almost everyone had to struggle to keep alive. Now, due to the productivity of machines that substitute for human struggle, there are many who can survive without much effort although there has been no motivational change. The primary goal for many has been merely to exist; now they can do this with less strain. Fortunately, the creative people, the innovators, the leaders, the top five per cent, still will direct the remaining 95 per cent along the path of life. The primary goal of this intellectual set (to provide a better existence), is the same as it has been for comparable groups throughout history. They will work hard to achieve this goal with a minimum of free time for themselves.

Technology not only provides more leisure for the vast majority of people but it also has a profound effect on everyone. Technology has provided us the means to control death and, concurrently, increase the supply of food. The net result of these two developments is the so-called population explosion. It could hardly be called anything else. To illustrate, it has taken man about 200,000 years to reach the present population of 3 billion people. And yet at the present rate of population growth this number will double in the next 35 years.

Nevertheless, the facts are interpreted pessimistically by some, optimistically by others. The pessimist sees the people frantically scrambling over one another in anthill-like communities in search of food. They see the stronger but hungrier nations waging war on the weaker nations with larger food supplies. The optimist agrees that the population will continue to grow at a rapid pace but that man will also rise to the challenge of producing sufficient food: the oceans will be "farmed"; agricultural efficiency will be increased; new ways to synthesize food will be developed; atomic energy will be used to desalt the oceans; the standard of living will be raised.

There is, of course, a physical limit to the number of people that can populate the earth. As a technical exercise, I imagine, Dr. J. H. Fremlin, physicist at the University of Birmingham, England, manages to work the population up to an eventual limit of 60 trillion people by the year 2,855. This limit has been set because the amount of heat generated by so many people exceeds the thermal radiation capability of the earth; more than 60 trillion people would cause the temperature to rise to a dangerous level and everyone would burn.

A well-known biological law states that living things multiply in geometric progression if no limits are set upon their reproductive powers. Under this law, a pair of meat flies (Lucillia sericata) could theoretically produce in nine months, a weight of descendants equivalent to the total weight of the earth—10 million times. Under natural conditions, of course, these things don't happen because life sustaining materials are used up. There is a lack of space for further growth and the environment becomes poisoned by metabolic waste-products. It is interesting to note that nature keeps populations in check without birth control.

The current increase in human population is easy to explain. Until several centuries ago man did not know enough about himself, or nature, to resist the attack of disease and death. The life-expectancy was shorter than thirty years and one-out-of-every-four children died before his first birthday, two-out-of-four never reached their fifth birthday. Thus, man's population growth was kept in check as were all other living things.

In Great Britain the population grew rather slowly from 1 million in Norman times to more than 5 million by the end of the 1600's. It then doubled to 10 million before the end of the 1700's. The same growth occurred in all other countries of the civilized world, a growth that is continuing in modern times.

It is easy to extrapolate an almost vertical growth curve to the point where all sorts of horrible consequences are possible. The popular—and often times sensation seeking—press seems to take delight in doing just that. But the more serious thinkers readily admit that predicting population increase or decrease, with all the census data that is available, is a most difficult task. While man is still subject to many natural laws governing birth and death, he can control others. Because of this, statistically-valid predictions of even the near future are almost impossible. For example, the current birth rate in the United States is surprising many, even those in the government departments who keep records of such things. Contrary to the public concept, the number has been dropping since 1961. But what is even more remarkable to the experts is the decrease in the rate of fertility (the number of births per thousand female population aged 15-44 years).

Specifically, with an increase of female population in the so-called child-bearing years, the birth rate dropped 2.4 per cent in 1962, 1.2 per cent in 1963, and 1.4 per cent in 1964. The fertility rate has been reduced some 12 per cent in the period 1959-1964. Total births in 1965 were less than 4 million, the lowest since 1953. The downward trend applies almost equally to white and non-white women (two and three per cent respectively in 1964) as well as to urban and rural areas. (Actually, an upward trend was expected as the men and women who were born in 1946-1948—the baby boom years—reached marriageable age.) While it is too early to establish any firm conclusion as to its cause, researchers point to the sharp drop in the birth rate that followed the widespread introduction of oral birth control pills in 1962 ($60 million sold in 1965). It is also significant that while 75,000 women received birth control information in 1963, 175,000 received this aid in 1964.

Sweeping generalizations with respect to population growth or decline are difficult to support, in the United States as well as other countries. Biological factors, although present, are not pervasive—there is no true instinct that prompts humans to have children. Geographic factors are not limiting: man has demonstrated that he can live and multiply in the coldest or most arid regions; nations with higher population densities do not necessarily attack those with less—the reverse was true when the Germans invaded Poland; the birth rate in one part of the country may be vastly different from that of another part.

What then determines population and why is it so difficult to predict? It is a combination of localized and specific factors. Under modern conditions it is only the rational desire for the pleasures of a family: desires that are influenced by social, economic, and religious pressures. This is somewhat changed from former times when a couple had to produce twelve children (six of whom would survive) to help with the work on the farm.

Religious beliefs vary widely concerning sexual behavior: marriage, divorce, birth control, and the like. Populations vary even in countries with predominantly the same religion. For example, most Italians are of Catholic denomination but the people of southern Italy are more prolific than those of the north who have one of the lowest birth rates in the Western world. Social or psychological factors also play an important part. In India, the man who fathers many children rates high in social prestige. Also, the Latin American concept, amounting to a cult (called Machismo), decrees a man proves his masculinity by raising many children.

While political and specific economic pressures, such as those resulting from taxation of family allowances, have produced short term results, the long term effectiveness of these measures is uncertain and unpredictable.

Most significant of all factors determining population are those attributed to our mechanistic way of life. Life in the city tends to reduce the birth rate as compared to that of the agricultural or rural communities. Family ties lose their strength in urban areas and are often broken as the industrial demands for mobility literally scatter children and relatives all over the country. While the cost of raising the children in agricultural communities is little more than the food they consume, there is no end to the needs of city children. Children on the farm are productive at an early age because their training is in the form of an apprenticeship. On the other hand, the city child spends all of his adolescence and young adulthood in school and to an increasing degree in college. He is not only non-productive during this period but he has to be housed, clothed, fed and given a sizable allowance.

Beyond these basic factors there are other social considerations which reduce the city-dwellers' fertility rate. The urban woman often leads a life apart from her family in activities which claim considerable time and attention. It is a fact that marriage is no longer an economic necessity for some women and consequently many choose to remain single.

Because the tendency is toward mechanization and its attendant urbanization, it is felt that the current rate of population growth will adjust itself and remain at a satisfactory level consistent with sociological needs. This level will be far less than one solely limited by available food and space. As our standard of living increases and we have time for more pleasurable activities, we will want to assure the same for our children, or desirably more. This inclination will result in smaller families—families which can be easily planned through birth control measures.

Who would argue that man is not a social animal? That people group together is an observable fact; there are more people living in communities than living as hermits or recluses. But is living in a group the same as being social? When we stop and think, several paradoxes become evident. People who live on farms or ranches are more concerned with their neighbors' welfare than are the neighbors in a city apartment. In fact, the word "neighbor" has a different significance. In the first instance it means a person and perhaps a friend; in the second, it refers only to someone living close by. Basically the country man and the city man are inherently the same, but how can we reconcile the apparent contradiction?

Let us examine a possible explanation. The person living in the country feels a need for his neighbor—a sort of dependence on him. This feeling or need is absent in the case of the city-dweller. However, if the two men are inherently the same, that is, both are "social," why are their needs divergent? I suggest that the city-dweller has substituted machines for the country-dweller's neighbors. Put bluntly, the city man (which is another way of saying the man of tomorrow) does not feel a need to form a relationship with the person who lives in the apartment or house next door; the need and relationship has been transferred to the machine.

Is there any evidence to support a man-machine social relationship? If anything, the evidence is overwhelming. Consider some daily social functions. Picture the sociability of ranch hands eating together. They pass the food to each other, family style, and joke good-naturedly while doing so. In an automat the food is obtained from a coin-operated windowed compartment; there is no need to converse with one's table partner. (I had lunch today in the cafeteria with the president of our company. What did he say to me? He said, "Please pass the salt.")

The automat concept has spread in the form of vending machines to factory, office, hospital, schools, and about any other place you find a crowd. The 6,200 vending machine companies in the U.S. did $3.2-billion worth of business in 1964 and this volume should easily double in the next five years.

The housewife used to shop every day, not only to purchase groceries but to visit with other housewives. Currently, so-called electronic shopping is being developed. First to appear is the auto-mated supermarket where all products are arrayed behind trans-parent partitions. The shopper inserts a coded key in a slot provided to make her selection. When she is ready to leave, the same key triggers a computer which assembles her grocery items from the automated warehouse portion of the store and also totals her bill. In time she will order her supplies by video telephone.

More about the telephone: Two women who barely will say "hi" on the street when they meet will spend hours on the tele-phone talking with one another. I suggest that the reason for want-ing to "socialize" at a distance is the impersonality the telephone symbolizes; it is almost like talking to an intelligent machine. There is no need to inject one's physical being into the verbal exchange as is necessary in face to face conversation. There is no annoying lapel grabbing, no need to pay attention to gesturing, no burden-some need to watch the other person's facial expressions. A person at one end of the telephone line can indulge in all sorts of verbal therapy. When the second person takes her turn, the first person can engage in such distractions as manicuring her nails, day-dream-ing, or planning the evening meal.

When the day comes that conversation machines are developed, I strongly believe that many will prefer them to humans as tele-phone partners—particularly the machines that are "tunable" to one's personality. (On the night I wrote this, I felt perhaps I was exaggerating. My misgiving turned to awe when later the same night I heard a commercial on the Telephone Hour start with the question, "Who says your telephone is an inanimate object?" The commercial went on to assure me that my telephone not only had a heart and personality but that it also served as a watchdog, staunch friend, errand boy, and more. Not satisfied with this, the announcer proudly proclaimed the telephone as being trustworthy, loyal, helpful, kind, cheerful, obedient, and brave. Not once during the commercial was there any hint that there might be another human on the other end of the telephone line.)

In any event, it is ironic that the head of the second largest telephone company predicts the volume of machine-to-machine informational traffic (data transmission) will exceed human usage of the telephone by about 1970.

Almost every new technical development directs our attention and actions away from other people and transfers them to machines or machine products. Spending more time listening to hi-fi or watching television, for instance, causes changes in the character and meaning of social relationships: changes which lead to problems. There is no doubt that the problems will be solved in a way which provides a fuller and more meaningful life. But to secure such an enjoyable life by substituting "personal" machines for conventional human relations cannot be achieved by traditional methods (which are all too often ridden with superstition and seventeenth-century moralizations). There is need for another new teaming of disciplines; the sociologist and engineer. Certainly a team such as this can find more scientifically rigorous solutions to problems of human affairs in a machine dominated world than the proverbs, adages, and maxims which up to now have been the stock-in-trade of those who set our social patterns of living.

I am not suggesting that science be substituted for ideals; rather that scientific methods be used for the attainment of ideals. There must be a broader and more concerted effort on the part of those who generate the fruits of science and those who advise us on how best to consume these fruits. In other words, it is time for the engineer to take added responsibility for the social consequences of the new and powerful technology he has developed. On the other hand, the sociologist must realize that decrying the effects technology has on society may serve as some temporary form of relief but in the long term it tends to add to the problem rather than to solve it. The sociologist should become familiar with engineering disciplines to gain insight into the principles of action in a real and technologically complicated world if he hopes to improve that world.

There is no universal agreement as to how technological advances should be controlled for the advantage of society as a whole. Neither is there widespread agreement as to whether technology can be controlled or even whether it should be controlled. Technology in itself is neutral and should not be labeled "good" or "bad." It is the uses to which we put new scientific developments that enhance or degrade personal well being and prosperity.

Technology allows us to be more humane than many would admit. No other animal cares for the old or sick of its species as man. While these kindly acts may not be directly attributed to technology, it does, to a large degree, make these acts possible. For example, among savage nations the old, the infirm, and even the poor, were of necessity killed or left to perish so that others could survive. Modern man makes every effort to save the deformed and retarded children, even when there is little hope for continued life. While some point out that this humanitarian practice leads to a rapid deterioration of the human race, others argue that this practice has already insured the survival of many great contributors to mankind's progress who otherwise would have been eliminated. Charles Darwin, to cite one example, described for the world his theories on natural selection and the survival of the fittest while he himself was virtually an invalid.

Throughout the foregoing examination of man's place in the new technological social sphere, generally I viewed the prospects optimistically. Many feel that technology decreases rather than increases human superiority and human dignity. They tell us that any bright outlook for the future is based on a false sense of security; a security which is as imaginary as the other dream castles we tend to build for ourselves. The increasingly sheltered life we experience admittedly does have overtones of a greenhouse existence—we are secure until someone breaks a window. When we think about the problem, we often find ourselves involved in a vicious cycle; the more security our mechanized way of life provides in the way of a peaceful and healthy existence, the more insecure we become. We visualize ourselves going further out on the limb of technology and, consequently, further away from the firm support derived from self-reliance.

Can the mixed feelings of optimism and insecurity be reconciled? The situation is similar to one that is faced by a group of people migrating to an unexplored country in search of a new homeland. Essentially, we are involved in a journey from the biosphere to the dybosphere, and are going for a good reason, namely, a desire to find something better. Hence the optimism. But one cannot be oblivious to the dangers of moving into unchartered regions; new situations and new conditions generally are encountered to which one must adapt, or, if possible, modify. There is little security during the journey or when the new land is reached; homes have to be built and sources of supply created. But security is established as a new way of life is forged out of conflict and hardship. In the same way, I am confident that future generations will solve the social problems encountered in the dybosphere.

Chapter Eleven

The Economic Sphere

When looms weave by them-
selves, Man's slavery will end.
—Aristotle

Technology has brought about higher living standards, won-
drous new products, reduction in disease, has made work less
strenuous, and provided free time to enjoy all of these benefits.
But technology has also brought disruption in the form of unemployment and mental strain due to the rapid changes in our way
of living. Technological change touches every aspect of our economy, schools, government, and business.

The future portends continuing change: computers might decide
when it was propitious to declare war or when to raise or lower the
Federal Reserve Board discount rate. Legal cases might be handled
objectively in seconds once the facts are transcribed onto magnetic
tape. Of course, not all changes deal with grim or cold decisions.
For example, Miss Little Rock Business Queen of 1964 was selected
by an IBM computer. It is interesting to note that while the selection was based on the contestants' educational background, business experience, and organization membership, the computer was
not blind to other important data—the winner was also beautiful
and shapely (35-24-36).

Both private and governmental action is required if progress is
to be achieved without diminishing human values. For example, as
our urban way of life tends to draw us away from nature (and at its
worst tends to destroy nature) we are in danger of finding ourselves
in an alien and hostile land of our own making. We are powerless
to solve a problem of this magnitude by individual action, for the

209

same reason, for instance, that not everyone can afford his own ambulance or hospital. The benefits of technological progress can be achieved only through concerted and knowledgeable enterprise. In short, we must understand the economic consequences of our new technology so that we can more painlessly adapt to its greater productivity.

The economic goals of higher profits, sustained growth, and reduced production costs are basic and desirable. But these goals have meaning in the over-all picture only if they provide individual recognition, satisfaction, and self-fulfillment. Technology—now, more than ever—reveals the need for a balance whereby individualism is not submerged in the demands of cooperative joint efforts; and where the demands for specialization do not lead to irreversible obsolescence.

If any single word can crystalize today's economic sphere, that word is automation. Of course, the term means various things to many people. To some it might mean their jobs were replaced by a machine, to others it could mean a release from exhausting work. There is no paucity of written material on the subject and the titles reflect the confusion—*Automation: Threat and Promise, Automation: A New Dimension to Old Problems, The Challenge of Automation, Automation: Blessing or Curse?*

What is automation? It is not the name of an object, but a label given to an efficient engineering *approach* leading to greater productivity, higher quality, and lower costs. Automation is not new. Its principles were used in a flour mill invented in 1783 by Oliver Evans, a Philadelphian. The cotton gin in 1794, the power loom in 1814, and the sewing machine in 1846 each helped bring automation to the clothing industry. More recently—and automation as a term does relate more specifically to the current trends in mechanization—we find it applies not to inventions but rather to innovations in processing such as drive and speed feedback regulation, interdependent machine-tool operation, process sensing and control instruments, computer tape and punch-card control, and process analyzers.

Put simply, automation is the technology of manufacturing or providing services as automatically and continuously as required. While automation causes unemployment and other hardships in given plants or businesses, it was brought into existence because of increasing competition, labor costs, product complexity, and scientific knowledge. In essence we have a tail-chasing situation. More automation is needed to produce more for less. To cite an example: Today you can buy a private aircraft that flies faster and higher than the Navy's first (in 1922) mass-produced fighter. And you can buy the plane at less than one-third the cost based on a weight and speed basis.

Automation is not only found in the factory; it is found in the telephone exchange, in the bank, in the office and in the home. It is being used increasingly in electrical power generation and distribution, in shipping, in traffic control and in the government. In other words no area of present day life is untouched by automation.

The problem is not so much one of furthering technological growth (it seems to be doing fine on its current diet) but one dealing with the economic consequences brought about by technological change. How are the benefits of automation and the costs of labor displacement to be shared? What role should the government assume to enhance or retard technological development? How should the government reconcile the frequently diverse interests of worker, union, employer and consumer? How do we balance the variables of employment, wages, and productivity?

Certainly the above questions are easier to ask than answer. As already mentioned, no single person or group can provide the answers. Nor do these questions and others like them need to be answered explicitly. The fact that our economy grows; the fact that employee and employer sit at the bargaining table and resolve the problems of automation as they arise; and the fact that the government invariably takes the right action at the right time in technological matters is "answer" enough.

This was not always true. The first Industrial Revolution of the 1700's and 1800's (assuming computer-automation represents the second) was marked by violent upheaval: social, economic, and political. More workers were enslaved than freed. Why (discounting psychological upheavals), is the second Industrial Revolution so much smoother than the first? There are many reasons: the first Industrial Revolution brought a high degree of disruption in going from an agricultural economy to a factory economy; educated people were the exception rather than the rule; and governments were conducted for the welfare of the privileged few rather than the underprivileged many.

The current "revolution" is not as harsh because the disruptive elements no longer exist. With many educated people, a modern democracy, and our current economic, psychological, and social knowledge, the strain of sharp changes is greatly reduced. The United States does not have to face the impact of automation alone. The explosive force of complete mechanization is being shared by many nations. (The first Industrial Revolution took place, almost in its entirety, in England and Western Europe.) Fortunately, the benefits as well as the problems of automation can be shared by all nations.

Automation, or the Computer Revolution, will continue to have a profound effect on our economic and political life for a long time. In fact, the rate of technological growth will have to accelerate if jobs and higher living standards are to be provided for a growing population.

As demonstrated earlier, a drastic change has the greatest disruptive effect on the generation experiencing the shock wave of innovation; but in succeeding generations the impact becomes attenuated as the newness of change wears off. I feel that when human-like robots are developed, their introduction will cause no more eyebrow lifting than the introduction of next year's automobile models. (Notice how fast we become blasé as regards our orbiting astronauts.) Consequently, we should not gauge the revolutionary aspects of automation on its immediate aspects but on a long term perspective.

Fortunately, our farsightedness is not particularly difficult to achieve. Earlier mechanical innovations were made without the benefit of a scientific base to explain the subtleties of their operation. Today, the reverse is true; new innovations come mainly as the result of scientific understanding. To give several examples, nuclear reactors, transistors, and lasers appeared only after scientific research showed how to develop them.

New technology requires mobility of personnel, both geographic and occupational. It will also require longer vacations and earlier retirement to offset unemployment. Guidance counseling will have to increase in both school and industry in order to direct people into areas of employment shortages. Communication lines between management and labor will have to be strengthened to compensate for the disruptive forces of changes in skill and labor demands.

We can all find a frontier's challenge in exploring and living in the dybosphere. There is need for the inquisitive, the eager, the daring, and the energetic spirit. We are living in a dynamic age which promises personal fulfillment for those with the foresight and drive to grasp the opportunities offered. Yet, the need for thoughtful planning and complete cooperation among individuals, business, and government is now more urgent than ever before.

Computerized automation is infiltrating every aspect of business. In some instances the infiltration is subtle, in others it is imposing. The optimistic estimate at the first unveiling of commercial computers in 1952 (that about three thousand of these electronic devices would be sufficient to handle all eventual needs of American business and industry) proved to be a gross underestimation. There were more than five times that number of computers in use after only a decade.

The first commercial assignment widely given the computer was the mechanization of payroll accounting methods. Then its application spread to the management of inventory and material control procedures. Almost daily, new uses were found for computers in businesses such as production forecasting and scheduling and control of complex chemical processing.

Computers are deciding to an increasing degree on who to hire and who to lay off. In the hiring process, electronic data handling systems provide a quick qualification profile for employees, including executives. Thousands of factors such as age, salary range, education, experience, and availability can be fed into cards or tapes and the corresponding qualifications of thousands of personnel can be matched to these requirements. The layoff process is the same, only in reverse. If, for instance, a ten per cent corporate cut is required, the computer can come up with the bottom person in every ten based on longevity, quality and quantity of work output, family dependency, future potential and so forth. Unpleasant as the layoff process is, it is certainly more objective using computer evaluations than the conventional human decisions which are heavily subject to bias of one form or another.

How deeply will computers cut into the decision making processes that once were the hallowed domain of management? Operating management (department heads, foremen) already has much of its work done by computers. Inroads are being made daily into the work of middle management (heads of engineering, procurement, finance). But the consensus of opinion is that real managers will never be replaced by machines; these men will be involved in finding new ways to use the computer.

Certainly the reasons for using computers are obvious. Computers perform lightning-fast calculations, store and recall millions of facts, and also present these facts in thousands of inter-related ways. Without these accomplishments—even considering the relatively short time computers have been applied—our economy would come to a screeching halt. Computers provide management control by telling where and how a company stands in its operations, even on an hour-to-hour basis. In the production department, assembly data are sent directly from the shop floor to a computer. The computer digests this information, calls upon and readjusts its memory file, and issues new production instructions and schedules. Jobs are listed in detail and in priority sequence based on delivery or customer demands (which are fed into the computer from other departments). The computer essentially acts instantaneously and, when properly programmed, without error or confusion.

Of course, not everything is perfect with computers in the office and factory. However, most of the failures and pitfalls stem from the fears and distrust of its users. This is especially true when computers are first installed. Many people who are used to performing their tasks by intuition or tradition are confused by the logical nature and varied capabilities of computers. For example, a manager through misconception of a certain facet of his job may never have had his error called to his attention. This could be because a subordinate, either deliberately or unknowingly, would compensate for the error by some devious route. Such weaknesses are spotlighted immediately by the computer system which cannot tolerate double dealing. It is understandable why many foremen and managers view the computers with distrust or the painful fear that their own jobs will be lost to the next computer added to the system. On the other hand, there is often a real danger of putting too much reliance on the ability of computers.

But invariably most of these problems are transitional. Fears and distrust are soon laid to rest and overdependence checked. Newer managers trained in the arts and sciences of computer usage are usually more rigorous, disciplined, and intelligent in their work. Procedures are tightened and there is less need for guesswork. Decisions are based on reported facts rather than prejudiced or distorted second- or third-hand information. Computers are neither relied upon too heavily nor allowed to be under-used.

Computers handle great volumes of information once systems development and programming work have been done. This ability is important in itself, but it takes on even greater significance because it can be tied to engineered mechanization (which extends and replaces muscular strength and manual dexterity) as well as automated control of manufacturing processes. Because computers handle information, managers are required to exercise new skills in the presentation of information to the computer. The information cannot be incomplete or vague.

Computers are being used in more businesses and in an increasing number of ways. Banks use them to plot optimum levels of assets and liabilities and how much to invest in every possible outlet for funds such as mortgages and bonds. Insurance companies virtually conduct all bookkeeping and preparation of policy endorsements, payment notices and issuance of dividend checks through the implementation of a "total system" concept. Airline reservation desks throughout the country use real-time random-access memory systems of instantaneous communication with a centralized computer: query, instruction, file, update, answer, and the like are handled at thousands of reservation offices and ticket counters.

Once the public has had direct contact with computer-aided operations as in making airline reservations or in banking, they become interested, but confused. The popular press adds not only to the interest but also to the confusion. Magazine articles and newspaper stories often play up the "threat or menace" aspect of computers and picture these devices as dehumanizing man while draining him of his creativity, imagination, and emotion. Other times the writers gleefully point out errors computers have made such as sending someone a check for $999,999.99 or addressing 735 copies of the same issue of a magazine to a subscriber. Another popular theme is to point out the odd or bizarre tasks assigned a computer such as calculating sausage recipes or determining which teenagers get tickets to hear the Beatles sing. Computers are frequently classified with battery operated back-scratchers or solar cell operated radio receivers.

By now, perhaps, the public is immune to this type of sensationalism. However, there are other headlined features of a more serious type. For example, the director of a United States department concerned with the effects of automation on manpower requirements has frequently been quoted to say: "22 million jobs will be lost to automation by 1970 and 12.5 million new workers will be looking for jobs in the same period." Generally, pronouncements such as these are qualified in unobtrusive portions of the subsequent text, but the foreboding message has already made its impact.

Certainly, automation in general and computers in particular will continue to change the character of business. The small businessman, for instance, is rapidly following the small farmer. In 1948 almost 70 out of 1,000 persons were in business for themselves. Presently the figure has decreased by about one-third. (Farm proprietors per unit of population have declined by more than one-half.) Large investments for machines are required for competitive and efficient production. No doubt this trend will continue.

But what about the individual worker? How is he faring in the Second Industrial Revolution? Is he truly being replaced by machines? What are his working conditions in automated factories? How can he attain a greater measure of security?

As already mentioned several times, automation replaces the need for manual strength and skill and computerized automation provides essential information so quickly that it is available for immediate use. To an increasing degree, this information need not be transmitted to a worker or manager. Consequently, the widespread application of mechanized monitoring and control improves the efficiency of production by eliminating wasted time and effort. This sounds commendable until it is realized that it is "people" who represent the wasted time and effort—and they are what is being eliminated.

Here we are caught in a dilemma. We need increased production to achieve a growing standard of living, yet increases in productive output invariably mean replacing workers with machines—automation. Almost daily we see that automation is accelerating so rapidly that it is consuming all the jobs that a highly stimulated economy can develop. We are told that the combination of automation and the population expansion will make it impossible to reduce the current four per cent rate of unemployment—in fact that rate will probably climb higher. Persons displaced from jobs by machines find it increasingly difficult to get other positions. Rising educational requirements make it difficult for the uneducated man to get on board the accelerating technological trolley car.

Although eighty per cent or more of the products manufactured by many of today's companies were not manufactured ten years ago; new products require new skills. And when these products have a higher technological content—which they most certainly do—a premium is put on technological skills. There is need for more scientists, engineers, technicians and other people who have a college education. Unfortunately about two-thirds of the unemployed do not have high school diplomas.

A growing problem is one that is affecting the unemployed who have been priced out of the labor market. Traditional jobs for the uneducated, unskilled, and untrained such as dishwashers and elevator operators have been push-buttoned into obsolescence by a $1.25 minimum wage. That is, businessmen find it cheaper to install automatic equipment than to pay these wages.

Since 1920, industrial prices and labor costs per unit of output have risen in parallel. But in recent years, prices have leveled off because through mechanization the industrial output can be kept at a constant growth rate. However, as a result of replacing men with machines, industrial employment tends to be kept at a constant level rather than a growing one. Yet in 1964, government statistics indicated that in spite of stagnant or declining industries, such as railroads, total employment rose by an additional 1.5 million over 1963 to more than 70 million. But again, while employment in factories rose only about 2.3 per cent (from 17,200,000 to 17,603,-000) productivity growth was higher at about 3.5 per cent. Thus even the experts are confused and find it difficult to explain.

What are working conditions like in highly productive semi-automated factories? The changes in work content and work environment, while not profound, are significant. In general, the working environment is vastly improved: light, roomy, air-conditioned, quiet, clean, safe. But the pluses are balanced by the minuses. While muscular fatigue has decreased, nervous tension and mental effort have increased. The change is not necessarily for the better, for while an evening's rest usually relaxes a worker's muscles, there is no such relief for taut nerves. If anything, the home environment only amplifies the nervousness. It will undoubtedly take a new generation of workers to tolerate the boring vigilance that is required to only watch for something to go wrong. A good share of the tension stems from the worker's feeling—and rightly so—that he is not in physical control of the work; he has "lost touch" with the product. Nevertheless he must be constantly alert.

The operator's job is generally a stationary one in which he mainly observes lights and dials and occasionally pushes a button or makes a minor adjustment. He is isolated from his fellow workers and there is little chance to chat or socialize. Time drags and additional rest periods are needed. There is less opportunity for promotions because there are fewer men to supervise: the job of foreman is rapidly vanishing. A promotion from operator to technician (the next step up) is almost impossible to make without extensive formal training. Because of the high engineering content of the production process, men with college degrees are brought in to handle the supervisory tasks.

Operators of semi-automated machines generally require less skill because there is little to do. Automatic machines are made "operator proof" with built-in safeguards so that unless the operator deliberately tries to spoil the product, he can hardly make a mistake. The most successful operators are those who respect and feel close to the machine. As might be expected, in many cases the operator substitutes the machine for the friends who no longer work at his side. This closeness is not difficult to understand when one realizes that the operators spend more time with their machines than with anything—or anyone—else.

We have examined the working conditions of an operator of semi-automated machines. But what of the future type operation in which the production process is fully automated? Human machine monitors (they cannot properly be called operators) will be expected to play an important but indirect part in achieving both quality and productivity. Automation is inherently like the little girl with the little curl right in the center of her forehead. When she was good, she was very, very good; but when she was bad, she was horrid. It will be the function of the machine monitor to keep the automatic production process from becoming horrid. This requires the machine operator to be continuously aware of all that is going on. It will be his responsibility to prevent catastrophic events which may occur only once in several years. This is not to say he has to actively think about what is happening but only that he has to be aware of what is happening.

It might be interesting to compare the machine monitor and the slave. Where the slave's work required brute strength and endurance, the machine monitor's work requires vigilance and memory. The slave in actuality owned none of the tools or equipment he used; the machine operator—theoretically at least—will be proprietor of all he surveys. The slave was motivated predominantly through biological drives; the machine monitor will be actuated through self-fulfillment by providing his mental needs in maximum amounts. The slave needed no special manual skill; the machine monitor will need no special mental skill. And finally, while the slave showed extreme dislike for his work, we can assume the machine monitor will show extreme eagerness for his.

We can readily see how a person can be kept in an abject state of physical misery. But it is not as easy to see how a person could be transferred to a state of mental bliss under the "working condition" which will prevail in the future. To have a worker perform tasks which normally he would not seek of his own volition requires that he be indoctrinated, as opposed to being motivated. Normally a person evaluates an externally proposed course of action and generally accepts or rejects it according to his basic nature and how the action fits his own plans. An indoctrinated person on the other hand, through some device, has the externally proposed course of action substituted for whatever personal course of action he may have had. In this way he acts to fulfill, often with enthusiasm, the "outside" program as if he were doing so on his own initiative.

There are two ways to indoctrinate a machine monitor. First he may be put into a state which is so relaxing that he stops thinking for himself. His thinking can then be supplied externally—but in such a manner that the person feels he is doing his own thinking. (Incidentally, this type of delusion is a more widespread practice than is commonly admitted; extremist groups use it constantly.)

The second way requires the opposite kind of conditioning—instead of a relaxed state, an agitated and confused one is induced. The result is the same—the monitor stops thinking for himself. In this crisis-state the person accepts the external program as a welcome relief from his confusion. Needless to say, in either method the "substitute" course of action must contain all of the characteristics and meet all of the requirements of a person's normal program.

Of the two types of indoctrination techniques, the first method certainly is more acceptable. And in practice it is not as "inhuman" as it sounds. To a large degree, when objectively examined, we are all operating under "Plan A." Our social, economic, and political culture molds most of us to work for the common good of all. Viewed in this light, the future becomes a little brighter.

The most significant, and certainly the most widely discussed aspect of automation is the replacement or displacement of workers. A widely heralded statement is that machines are eliminating jobs in the United States at the rate of 40,000 a week. Many feel that automation brings miracles of production, but that underprivileged groups are victims rather than beneficiaries. What are we to do with the 26-million young Americans who will be looking for jobs in the next ten years? What do we do with those who lose their jobs to machines, who do not have the level of intelligence, education or the working years left to start over in a new field of effort?

An economic theory that bears on the factors being discussed is one originated in the late 1800's called "marginal contribution" or "marginal productivity." The theory states that whether men or machines will be employed in a particular instance depends not simply on their relative productivity but on their cost as well. For example, if farmers could hire vegetable pickers at one dollar an hour, they would do so. But if they have to pay $1.50 per hour, they feel justified in buying mechanical vegetable pickers. Assuming the machines pick the same amount of vegetables as a man does at a cost equivalent to $1.25, the farmer will continue with the new mechanized arrangement. However, the advocates of the theory continue, if unemployment results—which is logical when many men are displaced by machines—pickers will be willing to work at something lower than $1.25 an hour and the farmer then uses men instead of machines.

While this doctrine of comparative advantage has merit, it is difficult to accept in every instance; there are many complicating factors. One is that when the farmer resorts to mechanization—that is, he buys a machine to replace hired hands—the machine's productivity can hardly be compared to that of a human. (A man would starve to death if he had to live on the wages earned in competing economically with a machine even as simple as the cotton gin.) But a man can find employment in areas where machines are not as yet competitive, as is shown by the increased employment in many of the service businesses.

However, we are really still begging the question: What happens when machines can outproduce men in essentially all areas at cost levels so low that it is not even meaningful to speak of comparative advantages?

Actually, I believe we are already solving the problem without even asking or answering the question. We are doing, intuitively or otherwise, what is called for under the circumstances; but we do not wish to take credit openly for the solution because the solution is so contrary to everything we have been taught.

I am suggesting that when man entered the dybosphere there was a reversal in the part work played in his existence. Until that point in time, he worked to live. Man must continue to work in the conventional manner until the "details" have been resolved and the new actualities penetrate into his consciousness. But the new trend has already set in. We mask this trend by believing that the major problem resulting from automation is unemployment. (This is not to imply that unemployment is a small problem, it certainly is not.) The major problem, however, is how best to distribute the benefits of automation not how best to have man's productivity compete with machine's productivity.

Having put the problem in this new perspective, we can return to the earlier statement that we are following the dictates of circumstance, but in a guise that is acceptable to our previous ethical training. That is, we are proceeding to raise our standard of living and, concurrently, eliminate the need to work at all.

Observable facts indicate that while the dollar income of individuals is increasing, the amount of work they produce is decreasing. There are an increasing number of paid holidays, sick time which can be taken when well, longer vacations, and 13-week sabbaticals every five years. In some occupations the standard work week of 40 hours has been reduced to 35 hours and less. Samuel Gompers summed up the situation rather well when he told the American Federation of Labor, in 1887:

The displacement of labor by machinery in the past few years has exceeded that of any other period in our history. So long as there is one man who seeks employment and cannot obtain it, the hours of labor are too long.

Work periods are being shortened on more than a daily or weekly basis. At one end of the age scale, young people spend longer periods in school before entering the labor market. At the other end of the age scale, workers are encouraged to retire early; even the mandatory retirement age of 65 may be lowered.

It is interesting to note the difference in attitudes between older and younger generations toward no-work periods. Those of the older generation feel guilty when they have no work to do and will either find some or at least give the appearance of being busy. Those of the younger generation have no such feelings over this and can be found reading books or doing crossword puzzles at their desks or work stations.

There are other ways to secure an honest day's pay for something less than the traditional honest day's work. Almost the whole group of service workers—from boot blacks up—have enjoyed increased wages along with those in manufacturing, farming, transportation, etc., but their productivity has not risen as fast (1.6 per cent a year versus 2.5 per cent a year). Also the quality of services received has not improved as fast as the quality of goods produced.

At the bargaining table, unions have found ways to share in the increased productivity of mechanization. In essence, there is little relationship between what a worker does, or does not do, and his pay. For example, under new meatpacking-industry contracts signed in 1964, existing pay rates are maintained even if the changed job (as a result of automation) requires less skill. Many question the ethics of paying on the basis of the end product of a job rather than on the skill or experience required to produce the product. Yet, the equivalent of this practice has long been followed by the railroads in their concept of charging what the traffic will bear;

the freight rate of a pound of gold is higher than that of a pound of coal even though the cost to the carrier would be the same.

An increasing practice in separating an employee's rate of pay from his work content is to create special funds from savings accrued as a result of higher automated productivity. These funds are used for the benefit of workers displaced by mechanization, such as in retraining for new skills. The Kaiser Steel contract, as an example, guarantees a worker full pay for one year at his rate of earning at the time of displacement by a machine. The practice of granting higher severance pay and supplementary unemployment benefits has led to the humorous but nonetheless true observation that this country's unemployed steelworkers are the best paid in the world—without working.

Fringe benefits are another form of paying more for the same, or less, work. Aside from pensions, severance pay policies, paid holidays, vacations and the like, there are company-paid life insurance policies; doctor, hospital, dental and eye care provisions; tuition payments for additional schooling; use of company automobiles; free vacation trips, legal advice, and even psychiatric help. Many benefits extend to the worker's family and continue after retirement. It has been estimated that by 1970 there will be about 200 different fringe benefits, representing a tax free one-third addition to the employee's wages.

No doubt we will gradually find ways to distribute the benefits of automation to the point where the work remaining to be done by humans will be handled by a small, elite group of highly trained specialists. Those who considered work their raison d'être will have to seek a new one.

If we were to select a name for the vehicle which is carrying man further and faster into the dybosphere, I could think of no better one than "education." Man has always been able to transmit knowledge and experience from one generation to the next. But until the advent of an effective written language—including mathematical symbology—there was no way to accumulate and efficiently handle this knowledge and experience. (In terms of the new technology, the concept of written language can be expanded to include not only printed literature but motion pictures plus the facts and figures stored in computer memory devices.)

Recorded knowledge and experience can be digested and analyzed, and the misinformation can be weeded out. Information can be passed on to others who can use it to generate new information. The effectiveness of the entire process of "organized intelligence" can be seen in the reduced lag-time between invention or innovation and its practical application. The net result of the efficient informational growth and dissemination process is an increasing number of highly educated people who can work in teams for the economic betterment of all.

But economic betterment cannot take place or at least endure for long unless all people, young and old, understand the new developments and challenges that our advancing technology brings to them. All must be given the opportunity to capitalize on technology's benefits and, equally important, to help reduce the undesirable side effects which such drastic changes bring.

Our educational system has increased in content, scope and method, to meet the challenge, and is in turn providing the fuel that keeps technology burning. In the 1920's only one out of eight working Americans had attended high school. Today four out of every five of high school age in our country attend high school. This trend hints that in several decades practically all working Americans will have a high school diploma. The comparable figures for college and university attendance are even more impressive. From less than one in twenty, there are now more than one-third of the appropriate age group enrolled in colleges and universities.

More specifically, the educational area producing the sharpest increase is that concerned with technical manpower. While the United States population has been growing since 1940 at a rate of 1.4 per cent per year, the employment figures for scientists, engineers, technicians, and science teachers has been growing at more than three times this rate. It is estimated by the National Science Foundation that there will be 4 million such professionals by 1970.

Other evidence of the rapid growth in our technological world is found in the rapid obsolescence of engineering knowledge. It has been estimated that the "half-life" of an engineer's knowledge is only 10 years; by that time after graduation his knowledge is only 50 per cent as effective for dealing with his job as it was when he graduated. Many feel the ten-year figure should be revised to five years.

Unless an engineer continually keeps up with the state-of-the-art through advanced study, he may find himself unemployable in many companies. This re-education process takes place mainly in "retreading" courses offered by most colleges and universities. Tuition is generally reimbursed by the engineer's employer, and the courses cover new developments in the engineer's own area, as well as new areas of technology. Other professionals such as physicians, lawyers, and businessmen become equivalently obsolete; but neither they nor the public are as fully aware of the problem as are engineers. Awareness and a concerted effort to improve not only enhances the professionalism of engineers but tends to establish them as the leaders of the various inter disciplinary teams they join.

Until relatively recent times the term "productive work" was used in the sense of physical output of goods and services stemming from muscular exertion. In fact our culture in this regard is based almost entirely on the moral and ethical "goodness" of hard work (although the Old Testament treats work only as a necessary evil).

Education—at least higher education—was viewed until World War II as desirable only if one could afford it or if one was to be a preacher, lawyer, teacher, or the like. Education was, to a large measure, related to leisure and the leisure class. The relationship was hardly casual for the Greek word *skole*, from which the Latin *scola* and the English "school" derives, means leisure. Throughout history there have been bursts of educational activity as slave labor released the privileged from productive pursuits to follow advanced learning and study. Today, machines provide such release.

It is not incongruous to say now that we have more leisure we have more time for educational pursuits, yet the relationship between education and work has acquired a new meaning. Education is more closely related to work than it is to leisure, therefore work requirements place greater emphasis on the more technical knowledge attained in colleges, and less on physical skill.

Before the crossover point in the late 1950's, mention of "the television industry" would produce a mental picture of long assembly lines at which workers were inserting and soldering parts into television receivers. While the assembly lines still exist (perhaps in a slightly more automated form), "the television industry" presents a different picture. Today we think of the industry mainly in terms of its creative writers and directors, the producers, video films, and most important, as a communication medium. The "industry" of television in this latter sense allows us to see and hear political candidates; witness at firsthand events in local, national and world affairs and observe other activities of significance which require our concern and decisions. Needless to say, decisions on issues involving technical, social, economic and political matters require a highly and broadly educated citizenry. In essence, therefore, while man has reached a plateau in his physical evolution, he is currently experiencing an almost vertical intellectual growth. It is interesting to note that physical evolution is related more to the individual, while the intellectual explosion is related more to the group.

We cannot be aware of the forces and effects of accelerating technological change and not ask where the expanding roles and responsibilities of our technical people will lead our economy. Already there is a change from ideas and innovations about hardware such as bridges, machine tools, and airplanes, to ideas and innovations about software such as computer programs, operations research, and systems engineering. The center of work has moved from our backs to our brains. At the turn of the century, somewhat more than two-thirds of the national workforce spent its effort on physical labor; the remainder of the workforce pursued mental tasks. This ratio gradually changed until the late 1950's (again the crossover point) at which time the amount of backwork equalled the amount of brainwork. The projection for 1980 indicates a reversal of the ratio of physical to mental work found in 1900. That is, two-thirds of the national workforce will be occupied in the tasks of formulating policy, generating and using information, doing economic research and analysis, designing new business systems, and so forth.

This reversal of backwork and brainwork orients itself ideally to the demands of the future. Too many of our methods and procedures are geared to a slower yesterday. To be moving forward, we must be looking forward. We must see and exploit the opportunities the future holds, and not treat changing situations as unwelcome deviations from the good old days.

Computer-aided thinking will increase the amount of beneficial technology while simultaneously increasing the demand for more technically knowledgable people. This is equivalent to the formerly demonstrated increase in physical production through the aid of machine tools which concurrently increased the demand for physical workers. And further, just as the machine-tool-aided worker was able to build structures and devices beyond the capability of the hand craftsman, so too will the computer-aided technologist be able to formulate patterns of economic concepts beyond the capability of the otherwise unaided individual thinker.

We are already witnessing the obsolescence of great numbers of engineers in technical fields that only several years ago represented the peak of sophistication and complexity. Hopefully, however, our new found knowledge will include the means for predicting disruptive developments in enough time to eliminate, or at least attenuate, their harmful effects. The engineer cannot solve all of the problems he creates. He must work closely and cooperate fully with those better versed in economic, social and political considerations. This means that traditional boundaries between society and science must be crossed and recrossed.

We have the power and knowledge to achieve every benefit we can envision. Until we crossed over from the biosphere into the dybosphere we were the prisoners and often the victims of our environment or of our own ignorance. This is still true to a large extent even today. But tomorrow holds forth a brighter promise, a promise which can be attained by working with and understanding our new found technology—not by fighting against it or rejecting it.

Chapter Twelve

The Psychological Sphere

"The heart of our difficulty is the difference in pace between hare-swift movement of the scientific intellect, which can revolutionize our technology within the span of a single life-time and the tortoise-slow movement of the subconscious . . ."
—Arnold J. Toynbee

No one can deny that we are in the midst of a change that is by nature swifter than that undergone by any generation; perhaps the tempo may even increase. Previously, the rate of development was measured in terms of the number of generations per major change; now it is the number of major changes per generation. Consider what has happened in the span of one lifetime—say, threescore and ten—starting at the turn of the current century. In this single life-time so many eras have developed that we are at a loss to choose one to characterize our time. This is the "age of electricity," the "age of flight," the "age of wireless communication," the "atomic age," the "age of automation," the "space age." Any one of these current "ages" would make the bronze age seem, by comparison, minor indeed. Yet, for all its onward rush, technological change on an individual day-by-day basis is so imperceptible that there is little sense of urgency to do anything about it.

Our world is changing. Technology is affecting man as an individual and as a group. What we are and what we become stems from our ability to adapt ourselves to these changes. Because we cannot halt change or always control its pace, we are forced to adjust to the inevitability of change and to its effect on us. We must examine the vital and dynamic forces in our environment and the positive and negative ways that we react to these forces. The present time in history seems to be an ideal starting point for such an examination. At any earlier time sufficient facts were not avail-

228

able for a realistic appraisal; postponing the examination until later would serve little purpose other than to verify the already obvious. The problems we face are already visible; technological change enabled us to move into the dybosphere. Now it is propelling us deeper into the dybosphere. As we proceed, we find ourselves in a machine-oriented world, and as we move still deeper, we will find ourselves in a machine-dominated world.

Popular writers enjoy pointing out the almost vertical rise in our technology. For example, Wilson D. Wallis, in his book *Culture and Progress* (McGraw Hill, New York 1930), reduced the period of man's existence on earth to a time-yardstick of one hour. The single-hour scale begins with the first appearance of man on earth and ends in 1930, at the time the book was published. First Wallis pointed out that the whole paleolithic (Old Stone) culture took 55 minutes of the total hour. The remaining five minutes of man's history was divided as follows:

Five minutes ago, he embarked upon the neolithic culture, the cultivation of plants, the domestication of animals, the making of pottery, weaving, and the use of the bow and arrow; 3½ minutes ago he began the working of copper; 2½ minutes ago he began to mold bronze; 2 minutes ago he learned to smelt iron; ¼ of a minute ago he learned printing; five seconds ago the Industrial Revolution began; 3⅓ seconds ago he learned to apply electricity; and the time that he has had the automobile is less than the intervals between the ticks of a watch, i.e., less than one second.

It is interesting to note that Wallis's technological development yardstick was based on the assumption that man has been in existence for roughly a quarter-million years. Recent discoveries now put the first appearance of man closer to two million years ago. Perhaps it is splitting hairs, but the figures in Wallis's analogy can now be taken as eight times too conservative.

Adapting to technological change is a complex process; people accept the challenge of change with varying degrees of enthusiasm and success. The problem stems from our not adapting to technology directly, but through the supporting framework of our culture. We accept and mold ourselves to change only to the limited extent our beliefs, training, and ideals allow us. Confusion is added to reluctance because the various elements and institutions which make up our culture are often in conflict with one another. When these conflicts are pervasive and deep, and actions are based on traditions, concepts, and customs which are no longer in tune with reality, we are in danger. On the other hand, if we rush headlong to embrace every new concept as it is offered, we are in equal danger. Consequently, we are well advised to judge for ourselves the best course of action and to keep the acceptance and rejection of new ideas in some sort of balance as we walk the tightrope of our existence.

One of nature's truisms is: adapt to change, or perish. Man and all other existing forms of life have made whatever alterations in their make-up a changing environment required. We cannot say that existence at present is a guarantee for future survival; even today there are several species that are marked for extinction. In the past, such as during the glacial periods, changes that threatened survival were relatively slow in evolving. Today change appears with lightning rapidity.

What used to be artificial is becoming natural; what used to be natural is becoming artificial—ground cover, for example. In the cities the "natural" covering is asphalt and concrete. We simulate grass by painting our driveways green. In the losing battle to keep things as they were, we plant trees and plots of foliage in small areas begrudgingly taken from sidewalks and the center of roadways. The flower boxes that once adorned buildings are now filled with man-made plants. More and more we replace decorative trees and bushes in front of public buildings with their equivalents made of welded scrap iron.

Yet a person can survive and flourish in an asphalt jungle as well as in a tree-filled jungle. The problem is not as much physical as it is mental. Man has to conduct the daily routines of his life in harmony with his beliefs of right and wrong, otherwise conflict results.

In the past when change took place more slowly, beliefs were handed down from generation to generation. It made little difference whether the beliefs were valid—i.e. based on scientific fact. The interpretations of natural phenomena, modes of conduct, rites to be performed, and the conduct of life in general were accepted by all without question. Significantly, only a few—the witch doctors, medicine men, or the priesthood of the time—were "educated" in the body of knowledge that governed beliefs. No others could question the "facts" even if they dared. So death, disease and the other hardships were considered the "natural" lot of man.

Today there is no universal acceptance of beliefs. Educated people do not accept doctrine and dogma without question as they once did. While this is a step in the right direction, not knowing what or who to believe in does lead to conflict. The conflict is increased when learned people argue diametrically opposing interpretations and views of the same set of circumstances. For example, the existence of God is being debated in various groups. A popular subject of discussion and review by many church groups is "what part can religion play in a technological world?"

The problem does not lie in our responses to technological problems; intuitively, or otherwise, we handle each new technical situation as it arises. The problem is relating ourselves and the question of human values to these situations. Literally we do not know whether to accept or reject each new invention. We know that technical innovation is significant; but the true significance seems to be beyond our reach. There is a growing feeling that the technological chariot man has created is self-propelled: it goes on without him.

There is the conflict of technological change, a conflict in which faith, humility, veneration, and the other idealistic supports of earlier situations have little or no meaning. The same conflict extends beyond theological boundaries. What of our legal system, our form of government, our social structure? The more lucid thinkers have already reconciled themselves to accepting computers as intellectual partners. Accepting a machine as an intellectual partner may not be too much of a problem in an office or laboratory, but it will be difficult to leave it (him?) there when one goes home. But, of course, our wives will have their "partners" to plan meals and figure the budget; the children will have theirs to help with the homework.

Conflict is an inevitable aspect of life; but conflict breeds frustration and frustration threatens self-integrity. When our self-respect, prestige, and sense of security are strained, we try to reduce the tensions through various defense mechanisms. In addition, to lessen conflict generated by an increasingly mechanistic way of life, we adapt our behavior and attitudes to conform to the new conditions.

Aggression is a fundamental reaction to frustration in which our behavior takes the form of attacking the obstacle blocking our way to peace and comfort or striking out at some substitute we choose to represent the obstacle. In our particular society aggressiveness must be carefully curbed to maintain social dignity as well as to safeguard life and property. Even grumpy attitudes and displays of temper are frowned upon by others. Verbal aggression (about the only form left for us) temporarily serves to reduce the mental and physical tensions which accompany frustration, but in the long run we encounter social disapproval and punishment which tends to increase, rather than reduce stress.

No doubt socially acceptable means for controlling hostile aggression will be found. In the early days of mass production, assembly line workers would scream, possibly every hour or so, to relieve stored up tensions. The many and frequently violent "fads" of our teenagers are other examples of tension breakers.

An even more drastic and yet still socially acceptable practice for letting off steam is the common Eskimo malady called *piblokto*. Eskimo women, mainly those who are cooped up for long inactive periods in their igloos, fall heir to this malady. This strange disorder, also called "Arctic madness," often takes the form of disrobing, throwing all loose objects in sight, and rushing outdoors across the snow shouting obscenities at pursuers. When the attack subsides, the piblokto victim generally falls into a deep sleep for as long as 15 hours. Upon awakening, recovery is complete and there is no memory of the event. Fortunately, piblokto doesn't turn its victims into homicidal maniacs as does the Malayan amok or the berserk rages of the ancient Norse warriors.

Repeated exposure to small amounts of frustration is a way to build up one's capacity to withstand greater amounts of frustration, in much the same way that immunity to certain diseases is developed by experiencing mild cases through inoculations. New generations seem to accept with relative ease situations which former generations found frustrating, simply because they are not aware of any contrastingly better situations.

One possibility for lessening technologically-caused frustration is for an individual to subconsciously regress to an earlier, more secure period in his life. He flees from the painful realities and responsibilities of his present life to the protected existence of the child. In one of its milder forms, the regressive mechanism is expressed in the "old oaken bucket" philosophy such as that demonstrated by the person who complains that "things aren't like they used to be." Generally, the best features of the "good old days"—creative effort or plain hard work—can and should be duplicated. Perhaps this requires a closer harmony with nature—fishing, hunting, camping, etc. However, careful thought makes us realize that we would not be willing to trade places with anyone from an earlier time, or even live the kind of life that existed twenty years ago. If we do not adapt to the current ways of life we put ourselves in the uncomfortable position of an old Adam who is not ready for a new Eden.

People often find themselves in situations where direct satisfaction of a drive or emotional need is impossible, either because the goal is physically inaccessible or because the behavior involved in achieving the goal would be painful or guilt-provoking. In these cases an individual finds a substitute for direct participation in the form of violence and sex-filled books, movies, radio and TV programs. War games and toys for children are part of the genre.

Humor is another example of compromise in which undesirable impulses or feelings are sometimes expressed, though less guilt-provoking and usually socially acceptable. Many progressive ideas to which we are being subjected would not seem plausible if presented seriously, but are accepted when disguised as a joke. I have seen some of my most radical concepts of life in a machine-dominated world appear in cartoons and in the comic pages in quite bold fashion. This happened on the day I was writing a portion of a previous chapter in which I suggested that machines would defend themselves in case of attack. A cartoon appeared in the comics in which an irate viewer was expressing his dislike for a western program. The viewer proceeded to draw a gun and was about to shoot the picture tube of the television set. In the last panel of the comic strip, the cabinet of the television set opened and a gun from within shot the viewer's gun out of his hand.

As a comic strip, this was quite funny. But I would be afraid to express the same thought in a serious manner, even though I firmly believed it. One of the best mechanisms available for adapting to a machine dominated world is a sense of humor; it is an excellent way to release and relieve emotional tension. With this in mind I always use humor when addressing a group on some radical development I foresee in our technological future. (You know, I think the "wee people" in flying saucers are machines originally developed by a human-like society on another planet that has long since become extinct.) In this way those in the audience who are threatened by the concept simply feel that I am joking and afterwards so accuse me. I do not try to alter this opinion.

When the frustrations and individual encounters with machine-oriented society become extreme and overwhelming, mild defensive reaction may not be sufficient to resolve the extreme stresses which often develop. Individuals who are unable to provide appropriate adjustive responses to changing conditions may be forced to employ some exaggerated form of behavior, or react neurotically.

A neurotic reaction may take the form of extreme anxiety where the individual has a feeling of impending doom. For example, there are those who feel that the world is soon to be destroyed by Frankenstein-like monsters or robots. There are some who develop phobias for machines which did not exist during their childhood. There are many who will not drive a car or ride in an airplane for this reason. At one time many secretaries were afraid to use an electric typewriter in spite of the increased speed and ease of its use. Many people refused to touch a telephone when it first appeared because they were obsessed with the idea that the telephone itself was talking rather than a person on the other end of the line.

Change is an exciting experience, but has aspects that many only dimly comprehend. The agents of change, the scientists and engineers, have little trouble in alleviating their own frustrations caused by the circumstances of change. They are aware of the nature of the revolutionary change of pace in human affairs and can adjust rather easily to the quickening tempo. And although adjustment for the vast majority of the non-technically oriented people may not be as easy, the long experience of the human race has provided an ability to absorb the shock of change.

Necessary to a reasonably smooth transition is the realignment of beliefs and attitudes to fit the changing world. Whether outdated or current, such beliefs and attitudes provide a functional

ving machine as the ruthless shearing of the tresses of his
her. Plowing the earth was out of the question.

he new industrial way of life invariably renders useless or in-
quate those behavior patterns formed from rewards and punish-
ts meted out by the primitive culture. The native workers
erstandably are in a state of tension as they learn new responses
unlearn old responses from a hitherto prized way of life. But
n order and continuity are maintained during transitional peri-
tension is lessened and new concepts and facts are assimilated.
example, the native who has worked with machine-driven ve-
es sees an airplane for what it is; his uninitiated brother prob-
perceives it as the sky-borne chariot for some god.

Io doubt the civilized observer derives some satisfaction from
ching at a safe vantage point of dispassioned scientific interest
dissolving of ancestral order and the eroding of ancient reli-
s certainties as primitive cultures are drawn into those of a
e recent vintage. But are we different enough from the "primi-
s" in our psychological make-up to smugly feel that we have
lly arrived while the natives are still struggling to get there?
ink not. Transition makes demands on the civilized as it does
the primitives. While various stages of development may not be
drastic for us moderns to accept, we along with the primitives
find the strains of transition difficult to bear.

'eople react to change in several ways. One of the most common
ctions is simply to dismiss a new or proposed change as being
workable. To illustrate, Simon Newcomb, the celebrated Ameri-
astronomer (1835-1909) stated in an essay that: "... no pos-
e combinations of known substances, known forms of machinery
known forms of force, can be united in a practical machine by
ich man shall fly long distances through the air ..." Before the
was dry, the Wright brothers flew their airplane.

The aspect of human behavior which seems to force people
react negatively to some idea has long intrigued me and, as a
ult, I have conducted casual experiments on how people react
"startling" technological possibilities. Although not based on
scientifically acceptable technique, these amateurish experi-
nts were none the less informative.

While preparing the groundwork for the patent applications on

utility; they give continuity to one's personal
ity in day-to-day relationships with others. T
raised, however, as to whether we can cut a
ented beliefs and attitudes to suit a mechani
we have to develop completely new ones.

Fortunately, or otherwise, we have to wo
exists. Even if a person had the foresight an
a completely new set of blueprints for orderi
it would be an idle dream to believe that suc
versally, or even generally accepted. Man rec
from his nostalgia and resentment when ol
are grossly changed. Current knowledge does i
the way a person will respond to a significant
interrelated effects of many changes. One t
with certainty is that even when change is a
an individual has a strong desire to accept it
succeed. A great step is taken toward accepta
facets of our man-machine relationships are
reviewed. In this way we can collectively de
changed, what should be changed, and how b
be brought about.

Any analysis of change must differentiate
individual and man as a complete social enti
individual is subject to the neurotic reactions
he seldom has any trouble, for inherent reaso
living in a mechanized world. The problem
collective group: his social and economic ru
perhaps his philosophy.

To illustrate, there are many examples in S
Australia, and elsewhere, of natives from pri
are recruited from their farm environment
After about a week of training they have littl
the machine environment. Most of the emotio
persist is a result of disruptions in their trac
and practices. What to factory managemen
efficient or a better way of doing things ma
direct rejection of the commands or wishes of
can Indian, for instance, formerly regarded

self-repairing, self-growing and self-reproducing machines, I had a series of illustrations prepared which contained the basic principles of such self-sustaining devices. Fellow employees would ask to see the illustrations and find out more about the "blue sky" work I was doing. The illustrations did not look like any existing machine, but more like human viscera such as intestines, lungs, kidneys, and stomachs because the illustrator had nothing better to work with than the pictures in a biology book on human anatomy. I explained the principles of self-repair, self-growth, self-reproduction, and so on, using the original art work which was in color and on 3' x 4' illustration boards. During the explanation, I adopted a somewhat tongue-in-cheek attitude so that the people could not tell whether I was serious or only leading them on. After the explanation, I asked what they thought of the illustrations and the future possibilities of these human-like machines.

In general, there were three reactions. The majority took a neutral stand: they were either not impressed or reported the pictures were pretty, but they could not visualize a working machine. A second group said they found the idea exciting and asked to be informed on further developments. It was the reaction of the third group that was somewhat startling. Some would turn on me in anger and berate me and my ideas, such as why waste time on such things even if they could work. Others would say I was tampering with things that had best be left alone. Still others would try to make some weak joke to hide the confused turmoil of inner conflict that was so apparent from their faces.

The conclusion I drew from the "experiment" was that the third group, consciously or unconsciously, could not face the awesome possibilities of the development of these machines. To do so would mean abandoning the concepts they had come to accept as fundamental and unchangeable.

Man is a highly adaptable creature. He can live, with the proper equipment, for long periods underwater, in gravity-free environments, and very probably on lifeless planets. If, with the exception of a few isolated instances (such as upsetting the diurnal cycle by rapidly changing time zones in jet travel) an individual can adapt to the worst the dybosphere has to offer, where do frustration, anxiety and other mental hazards of modern life come from? Certainly we must turn to the community in which the individual finds himself for an answer to this question.

General comment has already been made as to the conflict caused when there is a need to alter archaic beliefs and attitudes. Current literature is filled with soul-searching reappraisals of social and religious values long held to be standard and basic. There is not the space here—nor do I feel qualified—to review all of the long-held and deep-rooted doctrines of faith, convictions, and other commonly accepted ways of thinking. There is one facet of public opinion, however, that I would like to touch on: individualism.

Our society and government is based on the premise that the individual is the heart and soul of the nation. Thus man was able to enjoy a sense of personal worth by being a strong individualist. However, the trend of technological advances tends to slowly destroy the position of an individual as an individual; he is being caught in social forces beyond his control which tend to place primary importance on man as a team member rather than a "loner." This is true because situations and conditions are more complex and are being conducted on higher levels of organizational complexity. The successful sports team no longer depends on a star player supported by the rest of the players; all act as team members, each interdependent on the other. The same relationship holds for corporate management, work crews in semi-automated plants, motion picture production, and so forth. The one man invention, scientific study, business effort, or product is disappearing rapidly.

Somewhat paradoxically, an individual does not lose personal satisfaction when he becomes part of a well-organized and successful team although he invariably loses his individuality. As members of a choral group will tell you, there is a satisfaction in striking a harmonic resonance with other singers that a soloist never experiences.

But society as a whole is slow in relinquishing its admiration and adulation for the rugged individualist. Perhaps they should not; there is always room for the exceptional person. The fact that not everyone is, or can ever be, exceptional is the source of much current-day frustration. The social belief that insists an individual can achieve success only as an individual performer is becoming archaic. Loss of this belief is frustrating unless society realizes that a person can benefit all—including himself—in the humblest of tasks (and without, necessarily, any loss of dignity). If possible, a person should become a specialist even though it means joining a team of other specialists (as in a medical clinic or engineering firm). In other words, as our organizational pyramids become larger, they are becoming flatter on top. One individual is less and less the source of all direction. Rather, direction springs from a "grouping" of leaders. And within the pyramid itself, nominally-sized tasks are not performed by individuals but rather by groups (or teams, projects, crews, staffs, and so on).

While this "grouping" into higher levels of organizational complexity is actually occurring (incidentally, among machines as well as among men), society as a whole has not yet abandoned its old beliefs of individuality. Thus the individual who must depend on the group for his psychological well-being will suffer chastisement and frustration; and society will lose rather than gain. Realizing this, where do we go from here?

The current ideal of American society was based on the independence, creativity, restlessness, and energetic drive of the frontiersman; we vignette this ideal as "the frontier spirit." While we can be proud of our heritage, what happens when we run out of physical frontiers? We must find new, nonphysical frontiers against which to pit our strength, inquisitiveness, and drive. Whatever the goal, it should lead to the betterment of mankind.

The betterment of mankind has always been an avowed goal (even though some of the worst suffering mankind has ever endured has been through the misuse or misinterpretation of such a goal). But how can we give this goal a specific content that is realistic, attainable, and congenial with the characteristics of our time? Man has secured for himself essentially all of the material things he needs for existence: food, shelter, clothing, and much more. And he can assure himself a continuous flow of material comforts through means other than the sweat of his brow. Strength and vigor are no longer as essential as they once were. Hoeing, digging, building, and even fighting are more efficiently done by machines—not by men.

Mental prowess essentially has taken over as the key, desirable attribute of the successful man. But once again, machines (specifically computers) are taking over to a large extent the tasks of planning, designing, optimizing operations, and the like. Even the long-standing relation between work and pay is due for re-examination.

"It seems to me," John I. Snyder, Jr., pointed out at the 1963 Connecticut Mutual Life's Fifth Annual Human Relations Forum, "we may have to break with some of our puritanical notions along the line of 'an honest dollar for an honest day's work.' In an automated society, it is beginning to appear that an honest day's work bears little relationship to the honest day's work of the factory hand of thirty, twenty, or even ten years ago."

If carving an existence out of raw earth with one's physical strength or mental ability is no longer a goal—because it has been achieved—what new goal can be substituted? There is one that meets all the qualifications of life in a machine-dominated world. This is the goal of providing security for each individual regardless of whether a person struggles most of his life for it or not. As an ideal, security means not only providing the barest essentials of existence, but a high standard of living as well. The meaning of this new ideal is easy to grasp, but not the implications. To achieve the goal of security for all, society must first collectively agree that the ideal is worthwhile and indeed represents a new goal. Only if society as a whole bends itself to adapting to the new goal can the individuals within the society find their place in the scheme of things with satisfaction, enjoyment and a new dignity.

No one can deny that it was, and to an overwhelming degree still is, technology that underlies our increasingly complex life. That is, technology in the broadest sense of the word—the efficient means for acquiring, analyzing, improving and applying knowledge including art, engineering, and science. Technology is the vehicle that was used in the progression from prehistoric to modern life; a life influenced—and to some degree dominated—by wonder drugs, atomic bombs and atomic power, television, rapid transportation, and instantaneous communication.

Technology is physically real in the sense that the weather, the ocean, and life itself are real. It is futile to view technology as a symbolic idea or man-made precept in the sense that philosophy, religion, or a form of government are. We can change, and in extreme cases reverse, our ideas and precepts. On the other hand, we can modify our technology only to a limited extent, as is true with the weather, the ocean, and with life. Mostly, it is we who must change to better fit ourselves to technology as we find it.

With this as background, technology can be viewed more realistically and our adaption to an increasingly complex technology treated in more meaningful terms. To illustrate, no one is naïve enough to say, Tides are evil; therefore, we should control the movements of the moon. Yet, there are those who do say that the results of technology are harmful, therefore we should control technology. Certainly, the results of tides can be controlled to a degree; not by altering the course of the moon, but by dikes and breakwaters. Further, by understanding the effect the moon has on tides, we can adjust our shipping schedules to take advantage of this natural condition. In the same way, understanding the workings of technology will allow us to take advantage of situations we cannot alter.

This is not to say that technology is anything other than man-generated. It is man-generated, but not because of any capricious whim but because man is powerless (for many complex reasons) to do anything but continue to accelerate the technological growth that at times appears to engulf him. For example, military strategy does not determine the nature or extent of technology; it is the other way around. Also, in order to survive, a company has to develop a firm technological foundation and continue to build on this foundation. It can withhold a product temporarily until the market is more favorable. But no case comes to mind where a product was not developed because it was not a "nice" product or because it was dangerous. There has been no potent drug used by so many as the birth control pill. The moral, social and economic (in the sense of stabilizing an otherwise exploding population) consequence of this oral contraceptive will be tremendous indeed. All things considered, Western civilization must continually create new technological innovations to survive. And there is no reason why these technological innovations cannot be turned into technological "advances," such as using the knowledge gained from the atomic bomb for atomic power generation or applying mustard gas for the cure of cancer.

The emphasis should not be placed on controlling technology (assuming it could be) but rather on controlling the effects of technology. Instead of trying to hold back the growing tide of automation, we can profitably try to solve the problems of employee displacement and of newly found leisure time. If we are to keep our heads above the rising technological waters, we must concentrate on those aspects of our existence which tend to weight us down. With a better understanding of human adjustment to technological change, we can better predict human reaction and control the technological environment—*to the extent that it is controllable*—to enhance that which is good and suppress that which is bad.

Chapter Thirteen

The Good Life?

*There is some soul of goodness in
things evil, Would men observ-
ingly distill it out?*
—*Shakespeare*

Whether or not life in the dybosphere can be "the good life" must be decided by the individual. Nevertheless, the groundwork that is needed for making a rational decision can be established.

Man is becoming more mechanistic, both physically and mentally. Machines, on the other hand, are becoming more human-like in their appearance, their structure, and in the way they perform their tasks. These two trends are resulting in the convergence of a biogenic machine (a mechanized man) and a dybogenic man (a humanized machine). Objectively, I cannot help feeling that, relatively, man is declining and machines are growing. Not in the sense that machines are "taking over" in a robot uprising, but in the sense, that while man may only be around for one million years more, machines may be around for two million years.

Man has invariably felt that the "good life" is attainable only when one is in a dominant situation. Or conversely, to be dominated by someone or something connotes a "bad life." Either you are in the driver's seat or you are pulling the wagon.

Historically, man struggled against the elements of nature and, to a large degree, won the battle. Then man struggled against man, a conflict that continues to the present time. Whether this conflict is ever to be resolved or what attitude the victors will take toward the vanquished if the conflict is resolved is beyond the scope of the current discussion. The concern here is what happens when man finds himself dominated by machines.

243

First let me explain what I mean by machine domination so that the discussion can be viewed in a proper perspective. I use the term "dominate" in its accepted sense—to rule or control by virtue of superior power. In the conduct of human actions and affairs there are many instances of machine rule or control: we are awaked gently by clock radios, our driving is controlled by traffic lights, our pay checks are computed and printed by electronic accounting machines. These examples are hardly profound and certainly not sinister. Nor does the expression "machine domination" imply despotic rule or tyrannical control. Machines will "dominate" by influence and pressure or by the jurisdiction we assign to them.

Machines do have authoritative power (one is hardly aware of the extent to which decision-making prerogatives have already been placed in machines until it is called to one's attention), and as their capabilities increase they will be given even greater authority. Few of us complain. In fact we accept this synthetic jurisdiction too completely to be even aware of it. If it were bad or unwholesome there would be many cries of anguish.

To stop and think for a moment: in many instances, if other humans were to exercise the control over us that machines do, we would react negatively with feelings of distrust or suspicion. All of the evidence indicates that man has seldom gotten along as well with his fellow man as he does with his machines. Let me cite one example of how we "heed" the influence of machines to a degree unattained by millennia of religious teaching, decades of patriotic appeal, and the threat of prison terms.

Since 1962, the Internal Revenue Service of our Government has employed computers to check the completeness and correctness of filed income tax forms. The result is not only have taxpayers been rushing to pay delinquent returns but also, many people filed returns for the first time while others reported stock dividends and bank interest for the first time. In essence, these computers, because of their superior ability, exert a degree of authoritative control over taxpayers that is being accepted with little or no adverse reaction.

Still, the example leaves little room for subjective evaluation of the "goodness" or "badness" of life in a machine dominated world: the example is more related to empirical right or wrong than to good or bad.

A logical basis for evaluating life in the dybosphere is to compare the present way of life with the past. Nostalgia for the "good old days" has a tendency to put a rosy tint on the spectacles with which the past is viewed. Consider childhood: A boy knuckling his marbles into a dirt-drawn circle seems to conjure up a picture of contentment not found in the present-day grim determination of a Little Leaguer; remembrances of jumping into a mud-bottomed swimming hole in one's birthday suit seems to recall pleasures not found in today's tile lined Olympic-sized pools; the sheer exhilaration of the spontaneous games of yesterday involving a tin can and a stick or stone seems to have provided much more personal involvement than today's factory-produced and adult supervised games. But when I reminisce I also remember that my best friend, who shared those joyous pastimes with me, was stricken with polio and never celebrated his ninth birthday.

Obviously, there are good and bad features attending every period in one's life and in man's history for that matter; all black or all white interpretations are unwarranted. For example, those who believe in primitivism say that human virtue and morality reached its peak in the "noble savage" who was uncorrupted by contact with civilized society. Certainly there are elements of truth in this theory. But there was cruelty meted out in the name of virtue and morality (such as human sacrifice) that brings a feeling of repulsion to us now. Yet these primitives, for all their superstition, naïveté, and childlike behavior would have taken as dim a view of our present-day behavior as we do of theirs. Standards of evaluation are relative; there is no universal yardstick—qualitative or quantitative —which can measure the values or capabilities of one culture or age against another. No group of people are the sole creators of their civilization. Rather, they build their culture upon the foundation of their heritage and borrow the adornments for their culture from other civilizations with whom they come in contact.

An unbiased and dispassionate examination of the subject shows that the changes brought about by the invention of the wheel must have had a more profound effect on the people of that time than any invention has had since then. While the development of atomic power is not a small accomplishment, most people could not tell whether the electric power they use in their homes is generated by a water wheel, coal-fired steam turbine, or nuclear reactor. Granted, the pace of change may be accelerating but this does not mean that the impact of change is necessarily increasing along with the pace. Nor, for that matter, does change per se imply goodness or badness.

There is a tendency to over-dramatize our new found knowledge. Now that such characteristics as self-esteem, individual worth, motivation, and belief patterns have been identified and explained in scientific terms, the popular writers keep warning us that we are in danger of losing these characteristics. The theme of the warnings take the form of "During the last few years (or decades or centuries) certain trends and movements have tended to rob the individual of his self-esteem" (or individual worth, motivation, etc.). The writers go on to identify these trends—wars, automation, departure from Greek-Hebraic-Christian teaching, and so on. The writers tell us that the small-family farmer, long considered the backbone of the American economy, has dwindled to half the number that existed in 1930. The inference in statements like these is that our morals, dignity, and faith are also dwindling by half. But if the American economy has not suffered by "squeezing out" the small farmer, why should we feel that the personal beliefs and actions of city people are in jeopardy?

The childhood pranks of my day, indulgently tolerated by my elders at the time, now become the criminal actions of juvenile delinquents. As for immorality, the current generation did not invent it. We merely publicize it more in our books, newspapers, movies, and TV. For example, we view with alarm the increasing crime rate in our cities. Yet if we consider the number of murders committed in Los Angeles in 1853, on a per capita basis, and if we had the same rate of killing today, we would have the staggering total of about 360,000 murders in 1966.

The rules of the game of life have not changed, I'm sure, in the past 100,000 years, nor can we play a better game; it is just that we can "talk" a better game. This is hardly a basis for determining whether our future life will be better or worse than our life in the past. Yet, if nothing basic had changed in the past 100,000 years there would be no reason to try to evaluate life in the future. But with the appearance of human-like machines—machines which have and use various combinations of the senses, touch, pressure and vibration, heat and cold, sight and sound, taste and smell—there have been fundamental changes depending on the kind and amount of sensory input. Further, there are machines that react in some characteristic pattern which, in humans, is called emotion. While the majority of people would hesitate to ascribe emotion and other human-like behavior to machines, it is essential that we reach some sort of understanding in this regard.

Many people do not wish to think about, let alone discuss, the growing similarity of man and machine. To them a man is a man and a machine is a machine. There is little reason why anyone should convince them otherwise. But an increasing number of people are involved in the work that requires much consideration of such questions. Biomedical engineers, designers of computers and automatic equipment, safety engineers, cannot afford to put man in one mental pigeonhole and machines in another and then suppress thoughts which are common to both. It is surprising that the tendency to form logic-tight compartments to separate man and machine is strong even in these engineers. Several of my colleagues —known as human-factors engineers—started out in their careers as clinical psychologists. Gradually, these engineers became more "hardware" oriented; they spent an increasing proportion of their time working with complex machines and a lesser amount on the selection and training of people such as astronauts, operators, technicians, maintenance men, and so forth. Some of these former clinicians now spend 100 per cent of their time checking the behavioral patterns of navigational and computer systems (which do develop neurotic-like tendencies). Yet, when I ask them how they categorize their work, they invariably reply that their work is "people oriented." It is only when I point out that they are spending all of their working hours applying their knowledge and experience to improving the performance of complex machines that they begrudgingly concede this fact. For some reason they feel awkward or ashamed to admit that they have transferred their "allegiance" to machines. In other words, while accepting a modern view of machines intellectually, they remain bound emotionally to their strictly people-related past experience.

We are all, more or less, in the position of these engineers; perhaps we sense a feeling of guilt when we realize how closely and personally involved we are with machines. But is this feeling of being allied with something unwholesome justified? If the feeling is allowed to grow—as our personal involvement with machines will certainly grow when the machines become more like humans—can we attain a good life? Hardly. What, then, should our attitude be towards intelligent (or near-intelligent) machines? Or, more properly, what kind of attitude should be accepted as morally suitable? What standard of ethical behavior toward machines is the proper one?

I can understand the incredulity of those readers who wonder why such questions develop. Yet, whether one admits to the need or not, the situation does demand such consideration. What do you tell a teen-ager who says "I love my car." Do you say it is improper to "love" an inanimate object? (I am assuming he is not clever enough to ask you to define what you mean by animate and inanimate or what criteria you use to differentiate between living and non-living things.)

Tracing the evolution of attitudes toward others, we find the primitives felt a closeness (or kinship) only to blood relations. Slowly the circle of personal concern enlarged to include the tribe, then the community, and finally those of the same religious beliefs. Perhaps today we are on the threshold of realizing that long cherished hope whereby all men are considered brothers.

I suggest that the evolution of attitudes will be continuous and extensive enough to include reflections on proper behavior toward machines. No doubt there will be a negative attitude at first as the similarities between man and machine come into sharper focus. That is, differences will be stressed so that machines will be thought of as cold pieces of hardware to which no obligation is due other than indifference, if not contempt.

I direct the reader's attention to the quotation in Chapter 8 in which computers were called "morons," "plain stupid" and "feeble minded creatures." The number of similar attitudes expressed towards machines in magazines and newspapers is amazing. Relentlessly, we are being forced to form concepts of machines and their relation to us. Negation of these relationships requires that we live in a machine dominated world as strangers or at best in a passive role. If we affirm that machines are worthy of our consideration we will affiliate intimately with an existence in a world of our own making, and will be able to develop a harmonious man-machine climate.

What are the conditions that prevail in a machine-dominated world or, currently at least, a machine-oriented world? It is always wise to make an appraisal of how things are going. Today, such appraisal is essential for we are in an extreme state of flux. Anxiety generally reaches an explosive level when a person cannot relate his thoughts and convictions to something secure—to something he believes is worthwhile and significant. Until recently man has always identified himself with the natural and the organic. He found emotional security and intellectual satisfaction in a nature-provided environment. Now he is faced with the task of finding security and satisfaction in an environment of his own making. The task requires realism and objectivity.

Let us look around in as matter-of-fact a manner as we can at the world—at the mechanistic and industrially advanced world—in which we find ourselves. Let us establish a touchstone for surveying future expectations from present findings. The reader is invited to weigh my views against those he has developed for himself. I would not like to impose my light gray outlook of today's world on the few who tend to see it as being even whiter, or the many who tend to see man's future as being blacker.

This is a wonderful age to be living in. I am fully aware of the negative features of our times such as juvenile delinquency, threat of nuclear annihilation, vulgarization of sex, technological unemployment, and the rest. I am aware of these detractors from a pleasant life and need only to look at the front page of any newspaper to be reminded of them. But I am not as frightened as the doom-criers would like me to be. I have no quarrel with the facts; they are there for all to see. It is to the interpretation of the facts and the value judgments placed on the facts that I take exception. For example, the increasing crime rate is, to a large extent, the result of better and more honest crime detection and reporting; certainly the entire increase cannot be attributed to a weakening of our moral fiber.

The heated arguments involving the family and the schools, morals, art, business and government are not the result of chaos or decay but simply due to the metabolic processes of a dynamic society on the move. We have a lesser tolerance for injustice, cruelty, and superstition. Inhuman laws have given way to others more human. A reform movement without precedent in recorded history is taking place; a movement based as much on reason as it is on the principles of ethics.

Many point out with determined pessimism the mass conformity and insipid skittering from one minor amendment of civilizing reform to another. Seemingly, they look the other way when the masses meet arduous and formidable disaster with forthright bravery and grim determination. There have been many instances to show that civilization is not a thin veneer covering economic puppets which dance to tunes piped by computerized bureaucracy.

Civilization today does not demand blind obedience or ordained orderliness in matters of family life, education, art, or government as did primitive and historic cultures. But the fact that there is more freedom today in these matters need not be interpreted as the harbinger of anarchy or degeneration.

We do not have to apologize for the fact that our government, economy, and social activity are moving in a more synthetic direction; that the technological growth of machines increasingly supplements human function and complements human endeavor. We are not creating machines to replace man, but to aid man. What is required is not a decrying of the increasingly important role machines are playing in our social, business, and political institutions but a transformed view of these trends.

This is an age of contradiction. We lean toward greater standardization and fewer degrees of freedom in many aspects of current day life. That is, we tend to dress, talk, act and think alike. Yet we have a diversity and richness of experiences never attained in earlier times. Even the laborer of today has access to things and ideas not available to the royalty of former times: radio, TV, fast transportation and a host of other life-enhancing innovations. Further, there is hardly anything that the very rich of today can enjoy that is denied those with lower incomes: boats, foreign travel, automobiles, swimming pools, advanced education. Modern technology has broken down the barriers of class distinctions granting all groups privileges that heretofore were not afforded those in lower social or economic strata. To an increasing degree, all can attend the same movies, borrow books from the same library, swim at the same beaches, and be treated in the same hospitals.

A mechanized form of life allows us to perform bold experiments in art forms, educational methods, business techniques, legal practices, and the like. Surprisingly, innovation in these areas are generally encouraged and accepted by all. It is when we experiment to find new sets of morals and ethics better suited to the needs of a more affluent and technically advanced society that many gasp in fearful trepidation. For example, with the development of low cost contraceptive pills and devices, we will require a change of attitude toward sexual relations, with altered emphasis on such deep rooted issues as chastity, courtship, censorship, family planning, and sex instruction for children.

This is an age of enlightenment. Hate and bigotry are still present, but public interest and mass communication have brought these aberrations to the surface for all to see, to condemn, and most important, to correct. The need for self-appraisal and self-correction spreads beyond national boundaries. Because of global communication—written, aural, visual—people are consciously aware of disapproval from abroad, and have become more eager to merit the good opinion of others. In effect, technology has provided a window through which we can examine our own morals, ethics, and consciences as well as others'.

Those who express concern that our machine-supported society will fall into complacent lethargy should re-examine the facts. There are still too many threats to our security to allow us to be complacent. In effect we find ourselves sitting on top of a technological volcano. I need only mention the nuclear bomb as an example. Further, we hop from one crisis to another as our machine-filled world pushes us first in one direction and then another. We are more aware of, and doing more for, the aged, the poverty stricken, and the underprivileged minorities. Perhaps for the first time in any age, we are trying to assure that justice is as much for the poor as for the rich.

Good times are hardly ever dull times. We are living in an age of change; an age that compares favorably with the best of any time past. Difficult as it is to believe, we are profiting by all of the mis-

takes recorded in history. At long last we are learning to understand
the present world at the same time that we explore other worlds.

And what of the future? Can we project a better life for ourselves,
or will we take a toboggan slide down to despair and oblivion?
Obviously it would be foolish to make a generalization that things
will be either good or bad for all. In the worst of ages there were
those who turned events and circumstances into a good life for
themselves. Conversely, in the best of times there were those who
were miserable.

The people who will find the most comfortable place in the
mechanistic future are those who accept or, more likely, eagerly
anticipate a growing technology. Darwin's theory of the survival of
the fittest is as valid in the dybosphere as it was in the biosphere.
But, we must not make the mistake of equating "the fittest" with
the "strongest." For the time being, the emphasis is on the intellectual rather than the physical. What "the fittest" will represent
when machines handle intellectual tasks as machine tools already
handle physical tasks remains to be seen.

There is every reason to believe that the history of mankind as
a whole will parallel that of an individual man. Man as an individual goes through various mental capability peaks as he progresses
through various age periods: memorizing ability is at a peak in
childhood; imagination flowers in the teens and into the early
thirties; creativity blooms in the forties and fifties; and finally, in
the late fifties, sixties and beyond we reach the age of philosophy.

Notice how mankind as a group has already followed most of this
time-table. The cultural mainspring of the man of antiquity was
the myth, legend, taboo, fable, parable: all memorized and passed
from one generation to another. The Renaissance brought analysis,
synthesis, and organization to a peak as exemplified by mathematics, poetry, and music. Currently mankind is in its creative peak
period, excelling in science, engineering, and architecture. There is
little reason to doubt—although I can not recall anyone predicting
it—that the next age of mankind will bring a pinnacle of philo-
sophic output.

Several points implicit in the above analogy call for further examination. First, there is the admission that man is now in his

autumn period and about to enter his winter one. However, as mentioned earlier, man's spring lasted for roughly one million years and his summer (the First Industrial Revolution) for several hundred years. If we can use some sort of symmetrical logic we can foresee man's fall season (the Second or Computerized Revolution) lasting several hundred years more and then a winter period of an additional million years. Second, there is the implication of continued growth, but at different rates. Currently our civilization, after a slow, steady climb due to agricultural developments, now seems to be rising almost vertically because of industrial and technological innovation. Typical of the exhilaration of peak acceleration is the feeling it will go on forever; but this is not true.

There are two interesting characteristics of a growth trend. One is that the more there is of something, the more there will be. This is a characteristic everyone is familiar with: the rich get richer, the poor get poorer; the more rabbits there are to start with, the more rabbits there will be. But there is a second characteristic (described by the statistician Polya) that is not as well known: the longer a trend lasts, the more likely it is that it will decrease. The second characteristic is in many respects a fortunate one. To illustrate: In an epidemic, the more children there are who have measles, the more children there will be who will catch them. However, the longer the measle epidemic persists, the less likely any new children will catch the disease.

The two trend characteristics combine to generate the familiar growth curve that takes the form of an elongated italic $\int$. In fact, all living organisms, from bacteria, to rabbits, as well as human populations in a given country, follow this growth trend pattern. I would say that the same holds true for man's technology. Technology is subject to the second trend characteristic as well as to the first. The result being that man's technology will grow the more there is of it but will tend to decrease the longer such technology exists. In other words, there will be a leveling off of new human scientific development at some future time. Whether there will be a new surge of human technological growth (such as might be produced by mechanization of various human parts and artificial alteration of genes) from the plateau, or whether man and his technol-

ogy will plummet to stone age depths, certainly cannot be predicted
at this time.

There is a factor present, however, which should not be overlooked. Assuming, optimistically, that man continues at some high
level of existence, what about the growth pattern of machines?
Compared to man's, the machine's growth curve appears straight
up. Machines (as opposed to machine-tools) have passed their peak
memorization phase in less than a score of years—compared to
man's million years. After about five years, the machine has gone
well into its second phase—compared to man's 200 years. If machines are "nurtured" by man's technology, say for a thousand years,
until the machines are entirely self-sufficient, cannot machines develop their own technology? I see no reason why they cannot or
will not. (That is why in the previous paragraph I used the qualifying terms *man's* technology and *human* scientific development.)

One may ask what motivating force there will be to cause machines to "develop," "advance," and "multiply." The answer is:
the same motivational forces that cause man to do these things.
Almost everything in nature combines with like items on one level
of organizational complexity to form combinations which represent
new entities on the next higher level of organizational complexity.
These new entities have new and advanced characteristics of their
own which could not necessarily be inferred from examining the
constituent parts of the sub-entities. For example, atomic particles
are "organized" into atoms; atoms are "organized" into molecules;
molecules are "organized" into the constituent parts of a living cell
and so on until we have an "entity" as complex as a man. Certainly
man did not "organize" himself; he was organized from the material
making up the universe and the multitude of forces at play in the
universe. I submit that the same (or probably more varied, for that
matter) materials can constitute, in successive, higher tiered group-
ings, machines equalling the complexity of man. Coupled with this,
the combining of elementary forces (gravity, electromagnetism,
etc.) themselves into higher levels of organizational complexity—
to match the increasingly higher levels of physical complexity—will
result in motivational forces (comparable, though not necessarily
the same as such human drives as loyalty, ambition, love and hate)

which will cause machines to reach levels of existence (ontologically speaking) beyond those attainable by man.

Certainly man cannot disregard the past in planning for the future. But in the face of the meteoric rise in machine capability, there is no reason to be unimaginative or reactionary, and insist that past forms of life will be the sole guide to determine the direction and extent of future progress. Without question, the appearance of advanced machines will cause a mode of living which is radically different from traditional modes.

As a part of the world in which we live, machines operate other machines; machines communicate with other machines; machines design other machines. And, as we have discussed, machines can grow, can adapt to their environment, and can reproduce themselves. What is man's current place in such a world?

Hope and anxiety are aroused: hope for a better future through the fruits of technology, and anxiety that technology will create problems which will rob man of the treasures that it has placed within his reach.

Cornucopian abundance is fitting for the fairy tale, but how do we treat it as an actuality? Affluence is exhilarating, but were we physically and mentally made for it? Certainly if man could endure the curses of life he can adapt to its blessings. The price for the blessings is a calm attitude during the transitional period. Work cannot be turned into leisure as easily as darkness is turned into light by the flip of a switch: but on the other hand there is no reason to grope blindly and endlessly for fresh patterns of individualism and group behavior for our lives to be integrated into a harmonious existence. We can develop these patterns directly with the help of scientific methods.

Man has created new kinds of machines. Now machines are creating a new kind of man. We have passed the point where we could arbitrarily decide that the new life is not for us and that we should go back to the former way of life. Yet many cry that limitless consumption, long periods of leisure, and an extended life are inherently bad because they are "unnatural." We still have high priests who warn the populace that innovations which save labor or bring comfort are to be shunned. Nature should not be tampered with; suffering is good for the soul; man should be satisfied with things as they are and should not exalt himself beyond his proper expectations. Anything that eases childbirth is opposed to divine will; alleviating such pain is to "avoid one part of the primeval curse on woman." Even today we have countless examples of this approach: If God wanted fluoridated water to prevent cavities, he would have provided it directly. The appearance of any body substitute or prosthetic device inspires distrust, ridicule, or horror because it replaces a personal segment of our being. It is self-evident that these attitudes, if they persist, will drive us into oblivion.

Present-day high priests are not loath to use scientific or statistical data to further their arguments. They tell us to look at the high alcoholic, suicide, and insanity rates in the civilized and affluent societies. They point out with well-worded dismay the pressures for conformity and the tendency to become prisoners of the organization and the institution. While there are elements of truth in what these pseudo-scientists tell us, they mostly waste their talents on whipping us into frenzies of discontent (and perhaps drive us to the alcohol, insanity, and suicide they mention in their arguments) rather than apply their abilities to finding solutions to the problems of mechanized living.

Change is inevitable, and I believe the direction in which we are going is for the better. We must adapt to change (which is not the same as blind, unreasoned conformance) in order to achieve the same fulfillment in mastering a technological world as earlier men so gallantly did in mastering the primitive world. The challenge of being dehumanized by a machine is very much similar to being "dehumanized" by a saber-toothed tiger. If we do not accept and meet our challenges we will be annihilated just as the caveman was who did not meet his.

Those of the current generation have seen and taken part in the ending of a predominately nature-provided environment. We are now seeing and participating in the beginning of an artificially created and machine-dominated environment. As each had to make or find his niche in the biosphere, each must make or find his place in the dybosphere. To speak of a free-floating, carefree and utopian future is nonsense. The scenery on the stage of life may have changed and we may be starting a new act, but the theme remains the same—man's search for a better life.

Bibliography

Adler, Irving, *Thinking Machines*. New York: Signet Science Library (Paperback), 1962.
Allport, F. H., *Theories of Perception and the Concept of Structure*. New York: John Wiley & Sons, Inc., 1955.
Alt, Franz L., *Electronic Digital Computers: Their Use in Science and Engineering*. New York: Academic Press Inc., 1958.
Amber, George H. and Paul S. Amber, *Anatomy of Automation*. Englewood Cliffs, N.J.: Prentice-Hall, Inc., 1962.
Anderson, C. Arnold, "The Impact of the Educational System on Technological Change and Modernization," *Industrialization and Society*, Paris and The Hague: UNESCO and Mouton, 1963.
Ashby, W. Ross, *Design for a Brain*. New York: John Wiley & Sons, Inc., 2nd Ed., 1960.
————, *An Introduction to Cybernetics*. New York: John Wiley & Sons, Inc., 1956.
Bagrit, Sir Leon, *The Age of Automation*. New York: The New American Library of World Literature, Inc., 1965.
Beer, Stafford, *Cybernetics and Management*. New York: John Wiley & Sons, Inc. (paperback), 1964.
Berkeley, Edmund C. and Lawrence Wainwright, *Computers, Their Operation and Application*. New York: Reinhold Publishing Corporation, 1956.
————, *Giant Brains or Machines That Think*. New York: John Wiley & Sons, Inc., 1949.
————, *The Computer Revolution*. New York: Doubleday & Company, Inc., 1962.
Blackwell, D. and M. A. Girshock, *Theory of Games and Statistical Decisions*. New York: John Wiley & Sons, Inc., 1954.
Bloomfield, Lincoln P., ed., *Outer Space: Prospects for Man and Society*. Englewood Cliffs, N.J.: Prentice-Hall, Inc., 1962.
Blum, G. S., *A Model of the Mind*. New York: John Wiley & Sons, Inc., 1961.
Bonner, J. T., *The Evolution of Development*. London: Cambridge University Press, 1958.
Borko, Harold, ed., *Computer Applications in the Behavioral Sciences*. Englewood Cliffs, N.J.: Prentice-Hall, Inc., 1962.
Bowden, B. V., ed., *Faster Than Thought*. London: Sir Isaac Pitman & Sons, 1953.
Bowen, Howard R., ed., *Automation and Economic Progress: The National Commission Report*. Englewood Cliffs, N.J.: Prentice-Hall, Inc., 1966.
Bright, James R., *Automation and Management*. Boston: Harvard University Graduate School of Business Administration, 1958.

Bruner, J. S., J. J. Goodnow and G. A. Austin, *A Study of Thinking*. New York: John Wiley & Sons, Inc., 1956.

Buckingham, Walter, *Automation: Its Impact on Business and People*. New York: The New American Library of World Literature, Inc., 1963.

Butler, Samuel, *Erewhon*. New York: The New American Library of World Literature, Inc. (Signet, paperback), 1961, published first in 1872.

Cleator, P. E., *The Robot Era*. London: George Allen & University, Ltd., 1955.

Culbertson, James T., *The Minds of Robots*. Urbana, Illinois: University of Illinois Press, 1963.

Davis, Kingsley, *Human Society*. New York: The Macmillan Company, 1949.

Deutsch, Karl, *The Nerves of Government*. New York: The Free Press of Glencoe, 1963.

Diebold, John, *Beyond Automation: Managerial Problems of an Exploding Technology*. New York: McGraw-Hill Book Company, 1964.

———, *Automation: The Advent of the Automatic Factory*. Princeton, New Jersey: D. Van Nostrand Co., Inc., 1952.

Duncan, Hugh D., *Communication and Social Order*. New York: The Bedminster Press, 1962.

Dunlop, J. T., *Automation and Technological Change*. Englewood Cliffs, N.J.: Prentice-Hall, Inc., 1962.

Eary, Donald F. and Gerald E. Johnson, *Process Engineering*. Englewood Cliffs, N.J.: Prentice-Hall, Inc., 1962.

Feigenbaum, Edward A. and Julian Feldman, eds., *Computers and Thought*. New York: McGraw-Hill Book Company, 1963.

Feldman, Julian, "Computer Simulation of Cognitive Processes," *Computer Applications in the Behavioral Sciences*. Englewood Cliffs, N.J.: Prentice-Hall, Inc., 1962.

Finch, James Kip, *The Story of Engineering*. Garden City, New York: Doubleday & Company, Inc., 1960.

Fink, Donald G., *Computers and the Human Mind*. Garden City, New York: Doubleday & Company, Inc., 1966.

Fogel, L. J., *Biotechnology: Concepts and Applications*. Englewood Cliffs, N.J.: Prentice-Hall, Inc., 1962.

Fromm, Erich, *The Sane Society*. Greenwich, Connecticut: Fawcett Publications, Inc., 1965.

Fuller, R. Buckminster, *Education Automation*. Carbondale, Illinois: Southern Illinois University Press, 1961.

George, F. H., *Automation, Cybernetics, and Society*. New York: Philosophical Library, Inc., 1959.

Giedion, Siegfried, *Mechanization Takes Command*. Fair Lawn, New Jersey: Oxford University Press, Inc., 1948.

Goodenough, Ward Hunt, *Cooperation in Change: An Anthropological Approach to Community Development*. New York: Russell Sage Foundation, 1963.

Goodman, Leonard Landon, *Automation Today and Tomorrow*. London: Iota Services, Ltd., 1958.

Goodman, N., *Fact, Fiction and Forecast*. Cambridge, Massachusetts: Harvard University Press, 1954.

Grabbe, Eugene M., ed., *Automation in Business and Industry*. New York: John Wiley & Sons, Inc., 1957.

Green, P., *An Approach to Computers that Perceive, Learn, and Reason*. Proc. Western Joint Computer Conf., 1959.

Greenberger, Martin, *Computers and the World of the Future*. Cambridge, Massachusetts: The M.I.T. Press, 1962.

Guilbaud, G. T., trans. by Valerie MacKay, *What is Cybernetics?* New York: Criterion Books, Inc., 1961.

Hagen, Everett E., *On the Theory of Social Change: How Economic Growth Begins*. Homewood, Illinois: Dorsey Press, 1962.

Hatfield, H. Stafford, *Automation, Or The Future of the Mechanical Man*. London: Kegan Paul, Trench, Taubner and Co., Ltd.; New York: E. P. Dutton & Co., Inc., 1928.

Hebb, D. O., *The Organization of Behavior*. New York: John Wiley & Sons, Inc., 1949.

Hiller, L. A., Jr. and Isaacson, L. M., *Experimental Music*. New York: McGraw-Hill Book Company, 1959.

Holylock, W. G., *Automatic Control: Principles and Practice*. London: Chapman and Hall, 1958.

Hugh-Jones, E. M., *Automation in Theory and Practice*. New York: Oxford University Press, 1956.

Ivall, I. E., *Electronic Computers—Principles and Applications*. London: Iliffe Books, Ltd., 1960.

Juenger, Friedrich Georg (dis. by Henry Regnery Company), *The Failure of Technology*. Chicago: Gateway Editions, Inc., 1956.

Kerr, Clark, *Industrialism and Industrial Man*. Cambridge: Harvard University Press, 1960.

Kolman, E., *Cybernetics*. Joint Publications Research Service Report 5002, U.S. Department of Commerce, Washington, D.C.: 1960.

Laird, Donald A. and Eleanor C., *How to Get Along With Automation*. New York: McGraw-Hill Book Company, 1964.

Laslett, P. (ed.), *The Physical Basis of Mind*. New York: The Macmillan Company, 1950.

Latil, P. de, *Thinking by Machine*. Boston: Houghton Mifflin Company, 1956.

Lettvin, J. Y., H. R. Matturana, W. S. McCulloch, and W. Pitts, *What the Frog's Eye Tells the Frog's Brain*. Proc. I.R.E. (November 1959).

Lewinsohn, Richard, *Science, Prophecy and Prediction*. Greenwich, Connecticut: Fawcett Publications, Inc., 1962.

Lilley, S., *Automation and Social Progress*. New York: International Publishers Co., Inc., 1957.

Linsky, L., ed., *Semantics and the Philosophy of Language*. Urbana: University of Illinois Press, 1952.

Livingston, R. B., A. A. Imshenetsky and G. A. Derbyshire, eds., *Life Sciences and Space Research*. New York: John Wiley & Sons, Inc., 1964.

Locke, Wm. N., ed., *Machine Translation of Languages*. Published jointly by the technological press—New York: John Wiley & Sons, Inc.; Cambridge: The M.I.T. Press, 1955.

Lofgren, L., "Kinematic and Tesselation Models of Self-Repair." Technical Report 8, Contract Nonr 1834(21), Electrical Engineering Research Laboratory, Engineering Experiment Station, University of Illinois, 1961.

Lyapunov, A. A. and S. L. Sobolev, eds., trans. by Nadler et al., from Russian edition of 1958, *Problems of Cybernetics*. New York: Pergamon Press, 1960.

Mandl, Matthew, *Fundamentals of Digital Computers*. Englewood Cliffs, N.J.: Prentice-Hall, Inc., 1958.

McCulloch, W. S., "The Brain as a Computing Machine," *Electrical Engineering*, 68 (6), (June 1949), p. 492.

McLuhan, Marshal, *Understanding Media: The Extensions of Man*. New York: McGraw-Hill Book Company, 1965.

Mead, Margaret, ed., *Cultural Patterns and Technical Change*, a manual prepared by The World Federation for Mental Health, reprinted as a Mentor Book by arrangement with The United Nations Educational, Scientific and Cultural Organization. New York: The New American Library of World Literature, Inc., 1955.

Milligan, M., "Machines are Smarter than I am!," *Data Processing Digest* (October 1959).

Moiseyev, K., "Man and the 'Thinking' Machine," joint Publications Service Report 2200-N, U.S. Department of Commerce, Washington, D.C.: 1960.

Moore, E. F., "Artificial Living Plants," Scientific American, 195 (October 1956), pp. 118-122.

Moore, Wilbert E., *Industrialization and Labor*. Ithaca, New York: Cornell University Press, 1951.

———, *Industrial Relations and the Social Order*. Rev. ed., New York: The Macmillan Company, 1951, pp. 17-24.

———, *Man, Time, and Society*. New York: John Wiley & Sons, Inc., 1963.

——— and Neil J. Smelser, eds., *Modernization of Traditional Societies Series*. Englewood Cliffs, N.J.: Prentice-Hall, Inc., 1965.

———, *Social Change*. Englewood Cliffs, N.J.: Prentice-Hall, Inc., 1963.

Mumford, Lewis, *Technics and Civilization*. New York: Harcourt, Brace & World, Inc., 1963.

Newell, A. and H. A. Simon, "The Simulation of Human Thought," *Current Trends in Psychological Theory*. Pittsburgh, Pennsylvania: The University of Pittsburgh Press, 1961.

————, "Some Problems of Basic Organization in Problem-Solving Programs," *Self-Organizing Systems*. New York: Spartan Books, 1962.

Pask, Gordon, *An Approach to Cybernetics*. New York: Harper and Brothers, 1961.

Pedelty, Michael J., *An Approach to Machine Intelligence*. Washington, D.C.: Spartan Books, 1963.

Penrose, P., "Self Reproducing Machine," *Scientific American*, June 1959.

Pfeiffer, John, *The Human Brain*. New York: Pyramid Publications (Paperback), 1962.

Philipson, Morris, ed., *Automation: Implications for the Future*. New York: Vintage Books (paperback), 1962.

Pitts, W. and W. S. McCulloch, "How We Know Universals, The Perception of Auditory and Visual Forms," Bulletin of Mathematic Biophysics, 9, 1947.

Rosenblatt, F., *Principles of Neurodynamics*. Washington, D.C.: Spartan, 1962.

Sayre, Kenneth M. and Frederick J. Crosson, eds., *The Modeling of Mind, Computer & Intelligence*. Notre Dame, Indiana: University of Notre Dame Press, 1963.

Schumpeter, Joseph A., *Capitalism, Socialism, and Democracy*, 3rd ed. New York: Harper & Row, 1950.

Shannon, C. E. and J. McCarthey, eds., *Automata Studies*, No. 34, Princeton University Press, 1956.

———— and W. Weaver, *The Mathematical Theory of Communication*. Urbana, Illinois: University of Illinois Press, 1949.

Simon, Herbert Alexander, *Models of Man*. New York: John Wiley & Sons, Inc., 1957.

Sluckin, W., *Minds and Machines*. London: Pelican, Baltimore: Penguin, 1954.

Smelser, Neil J., *The Sociology of Economic Life*. Englewood Cliffs, N.J.: Prentice-Hall, Inc., 1963, p. 106.

Soule, George, *The Shape of Tomorrow*. New York: New American Library, Signet, 1958.

————, *Time for Living*. New York: Viking Press, Inc., 1955.

Stevens, M. E., "Automatic Character Recognition," a State-of-the-art Report, NBS Technical Note 112, PB No. 161613, Washington, D.C.: 1961.

Strehl, Rolf, *The Robots are Among Us*. New York and London: Arco Publishers, 1955.

Sutherland, W. R., M. G. Mugglin and I. Sutherland, "An Electromechanical Model of Simple Animals," *Computers and Automation*, 1958.

Taube, M., *Computers and Common Sense, The Myth of Thinking Machines*. New York: Columbia, 1961.

Thomson, Sir George, *The Foreseeable Future*. London: Cambridge University Press, 1955.

Tsien, H. A., *Engineering Cybernetics*. New York: McGraw-Hill Book Company, 1954.

Usher, A. P., *The History of Mechanical Inventions*. Boston: Beacon Press, 1959.

Von Foerster, H. and G. Pask, "A Predictive Model for Self Organizing Systems," *Cybernetica*, 4, 1960 and 1, 1961.

———— and G. W. Zopf, Jr., eds., *Principles of Self-Organization*. New York: Pergamon, 1961.

von Neumann, J., *The Computer and the Brain*. New Haven, Connecticut: Yale University Press, 1958.

———— and O. Morgenstern, *Theory of Games and Economic Behavior*. Princeton, New Jersey: Princeton, 1947.

Walker, Charles R. and Robert H. Guest, *The Man on the Assembly Line*. Cambridge: Harvard University Press, 1952.

————, *Modern Technology and Civilization*. New York: McGraw-Hill Book Company, 1962.

Warfield, John N., *Introduction to Electronic Analog Computers*. Englewood Cliffs, N.J.: Prentice-Hall, Inc., 1959.

White, Lynn, *Medieval Technology and Social Change*. Fair Lawn, New Jersey: Oxford University Press, 1962.

Wiener, Norbert, *Cybernetics*. New York: John Wiley & Sons, Inc., 1948.

————, *Cybernetics, Control and Communication in the Animal and the Machine*. New York: John Wiley & Sons, Inc., 1948.

————, *God and Golem, Inc.* Cambridge: The M.I.T. Press, 1964.

————, *The Human Use of Human Beings*. New York: Doubleday & Company, Inc., Anchor Books, 1954.

Woodbury, David O., *Let ERMA Do It: The Full Story of Automation*. New York: Harcourt, Brace & Company, Inc., 1956.

Wooldridge, D. E., *The Machinery of the Brain*. New York: McGraw-Hill Book Company, 1963.

Symposia

Jeffres, L. A., ed., "Cerebral Mechanisms in Behavior": "The Hixon Symposium," New York: John Wiley & Sons, Inc.; London: Chapman & Hall, 1951.

Markham, Charles, ed., "Jobs, Men, and Machines": "Problems of Automation," conference on solution to problems of automation and employment, New York: 1963. New York: Frederick A. Praeger, 1964.

Maxfield, Myles, Arthur Callahan and Lawrence J. Fogel, "Biophysics and Cybernetic Systems," Proceedings of the Second Cybernetic Sciences Symposium sponsored by the Office of Naval Research and the Allan Hancock Foundation. Washington, D.C.: Spartan Books, Inc., London: Macmillan & Co., Ltd., 1965.

Yovitts, M. and S. Cameron, eds., *Self-Organizing Systems*. New York: Pergamon, 1960.

Index